Hypothesis

AN INTUITIVE GUIDE FOR MAKING DATA DRIVEN DECISIONS

Jim Frost

Statistics By Jim Publishing

STATE COLLEGE, PENNSYLVANIA

U.S.A.

Published by: Statistics By Jim Publishing

State College, PA 16801

Visit the author's website: statisticsbyjim.com

To contact the author, please email: jim@statisticsbyjim.com

Quantity sales. Special discounts are available on quantity purchases. For details, contact the email address above.

Hypothesis Testing: An Intuitive Guide for Making Data Driven Decisions / Jim Frost. —1st ed.

ISBN 978-1-7354311-5-4

Contents

The best thing about being a statistician is that you get to play in everyone's backyard.

–John Tukey

Goals for this Book

In today's data-driven world, we hear about making decisions based on the data all the time. Hypothesis testing plays a crucial role in that process, whether you're in academia, making business decisions, or in quality improvement. Without hypothesis tests, you risk drawing the wrong conclusions and making bad decisions. That can be costly, either in business dollars or for your reputation as an analyst or scientist.

Chances are high that you'll need a working knowledge of hypothesis testing to produce new findings yourself and to understand the work of others. The world today produces more analyses designed to influence you than ever before. Are you ready for it?

By reading this book, you will build a solid foundation for understanding hypothesis tests and become confident that you know when to use each type of test, how to use them properly to obtain reliable results, and how to interpret the results correctly. I present a wide variety of tests that assess characteristics of different data types.

Statistics is the science of learning from data, and hypothesis tests are a vital tool in that process. These tests assess your data using a specific approach to determine whether your results are statistically significant. Hypothesis tests allow you to use a relatively small random sample to draw conclusions about entire populations. That process is fascinating.

I also want you to comprehend what significance truly means in this context. To accomplish these goals, I'm going to teach you how these tests work using an intuitive approach, which helps you fully understand the results.

Hypothesis testing occurs near the end of a long sequence of events. It occurs after you designed your experiment or study, collected a representative sample, randomly assigned subjects, controlled conditions as needed, and collected your data. That sequence varies depending on the specifics of your study.

For example, is it a randomized trial or an observational study? Does it involve people? Does your design allow you to identify causation rather than mere correlation? Similarly, the challenges you'll face along the way can vary widely depending on the nature of your subject and the type of data. There are considerations every step of the way that determine whether your study will produce valid results.

Consequently, hypothesis testing builds on a broad range of statistical knowledge, such as inferential statistics, experimental design, measures of central tendency and variability, data types, and probability distributions to name a few. Your hypothesis testing journey will be easier if you are already familiar with these concepts. I'll review some of that information in this book, but I focus on the hypothesis tests. If you need a refresher, consider reading my *Introduction to Statistics* book.

You'll notice that there are not many equations in this book. After all, you should let your statistical software handle the calculations while you focus on understanding your results. Consequently, I emphasize the concepts and practices that you'll need to know to perform the analysis and interpret the results correctly. I'll use more graphs than equations! If you need the equations, you'll find them in most textbooks.

In particular, I use many probability distribution plots. Probability distributions are vital components of hypothesis tests. Keep in mind that these plots use complex equations to display the distribution curves and calculate relevant probabilities. I prefer to show you the graphs so you understand the process rather than working through equations!

Throughout this book, I use Minitab statistical software. However, this book is not about teaching particular software but rather how to perform, understand, and interpret hypothesis testing. All common statistical software packages should be able to perform the analyses that I show. There is nothing in here that is unique to Minitab.

For the examples in this book, I use datasets that you can download for free from my website so you can learn by doing. I also provide links to free software I use in this book, Statistics101 and G*Power. I include scripts I wrote that work with Statistics101, which I use in some of the examples. To obtain these files, go to:

https://statisticsbyjim.com/hypothesistesting

CHAPTER 1

Fundamental Concepts

Let's start by cutting to the chase. What is a hypothesis test?

A hypothesis test is a statistical procedure that allows you to use a sample to draw conclusions about an entire population. More specifically, a hypothesis test evaluates two mutually exclusive statements about the population and determines which statement the data support. These two statements are the hypotheses that the procedure tests.

Throughout this book, I'll remind you that these procedures use evidence in samples to make inferences about the characteristics of populations. I want to drive that point home because it's the entire reason for hypothesis testing. Unfortunately, analysts often forget the rationale!

But we're getting ahead of ourselves.

Let's cover some basic hypothesis testing terms that you need to know. We'll cover all these terms in much more detail throughout the book. For now, this chapter provides an overview to show you the relationships between these crucial concepts.

Hypothesis testing is a procedure in inferential statistics. To draw reliable conclusions from a sample, you need to appreciate the differences between descriptive statistics and inferential statistics.

Descriptive vs. Inferential Statistics

Descriptive statistics summarize data for a group that you choose. This process allows you to understand that specific set of observations.

Descriptive statistics describe a sample. That's pretty straightforward. You simply take a group that you're interested in, record data about the group members, and then use summary statistics and graphs to present the group properties. With descriptive statistics, there is no uncertainty because you are describing only the people or items that you actually measure. For instance, if you measure test scores in two classes, you know the precise means for both groups and can state with no uncertainty which one has a higher mean. You're not trying to infer properties about a larger population.

However, if you want to draw inferences about a population, there are suddenly more issues you need to address. We're now moving into inferential statistics. Drawing inferences about a population is particularly important in science where we want to apply the results to a larger population, not just the specific sample in the study. For example, if we're testing a new medication, we don't want to know that it works only for the small, select experimental group. We want to infer that it will be effective for a larger population. We want to generalize the sample results to people outside the sample.

Inferential statistics takes data from a sample and makes inferences about the larger population from which the sample was drawn. Consequently, we need to have confidence that our sample accurately reflects the population. This requirement affects our process. At a broad level, we must do the following:

1. Define the population we are studying.
2. Draw a representative sample from that population.
3. Use analyses that incorporate the sampling error.

We don't get to pick a convenient group. Instead, random sampling allows us to have confidence that the sample represents the population. This process is a primary method for obtaining samples that mirrors the population on average. Random sampling produces statistics, such as the mean, that do not tend to be too high or too low. Using a random sample, we can generalize from the sample to the broader population.

While samples are much more practical and less expensive to work with, there are tradeoffs. Typically, we learn about the population by drawing a relatively small sample from it. We are a very long way off from measuring all people or objects in that population. Consequently, when you estimate the properties of a population from a sample, the sample statistics are unlikely to equal the actual population value exactly. For instance, your sample mean is unlikely to equal the population mean. The difference between the sample statistic and the population value is the sampling error.

You gain tremendous benefits by working with a random sample drawn from a population. In most cases, it is simply impossible to measure the entire population to understand its properties. The alternative is to gather a random sample and then use hypothesis testing to analyze the sample data. However, a crucial point to remember is that hypothesis tests make assumptions about the data collection process. For instance, these tests assume that the data were collected using a method that tends to produce representative samples. After all, if the sample isn't similar to the population, you won't be able to use the sample to draw conclusions about the population.

Random sampling is the most commonly known method for obtaining an unbiased, representative sample, but there are other techniques.

That discussion goes beyond this book, but my *Introduction to Statistics* book describes some of the other procedures.

Population Parameters vs. Sample Statistics

A parameter is a value that describes a characteristic of an entire population, such as the population mean. Because you can rarely measure an entire population, you usually don't know the real value of a parameter. In fact, parameter values are almost always unknowable. While we don't know the value, it definitely exists.

For example, the average height of adult women in the United States is a parameter that has an exact value—we just don't know what it is!

The population mean and standard deviation are two common parameters. In statistics, Greek symbols usually represent population parameters, such as μ (mu) for the mean and σ (sigma) for the standard deviation.

A statistic is a characteristic of a sample. If you collect a sample and calculate the mean and standard deviation, these are sample statistics. Inferential statistics allow you to use sample statistics to make conclusions about a population. However, to draw valid conclusions, you must use representative sampling techniques. These techniques help ensure that samples produce unbiased estimates. Biased estimates are systematically too high or too low. You want unbiased estimates because they are correct on average. Use random sampling and other representative sampling methodologies to obtain unbiased estimates.

In inferential statistics, we use sample statistics to estimate population parameters. For example, if we collect a random sample of adult women in the United States and measure their heights, we can calculate the sample mean and use it as an unbiased estimate of the population mean. We can also create confidence intervals to obtain a range that the actual population value likely falls within.

Population Parameter	Sample Statistic
Mu (μ)	Sample mean
Sigma (σ)	Sample standard deviation

Random Sampling Error

When you have a representative sample, the sample mean and other characteristics are unlikely to equal the population values exactly. The sample is similar to the population, but it is never identical to the population.

The differences between sample statistics and population parameters are known as sampling error. If you want to use samples to make inferences about populations, you need statistical methods that incorporate estimates of sampling error. As you'll learn, sampling error blurs the line between real effects and random variations caused by sampling. Hypothesis testing helps you separate those two possibilities.

Because population parameters are unknown, we also never know exactly the sampling error for a study. However, using hypothesis testing, we can estimate the error and factor it into the test results.

Parametric versus Nonparametric Analyses

Parametric statistics is a branch of statistics that assumes sample data come from populations that are adequately modeled by probability distributions with a set of parameters. Parametric analyses are the most common statistical methods and this book focuses on them. Consequently, you will see many references to probability distributions, probability distribution plots, parameter estimates, and assumptions about your data following a particular distribution (often the normal distribution) throughout this book.

Conversely, nonparametric tests don't assume that your data follow a particular distribution. While this book doesn't emphasize those methods, I cover some of them in the last chapter so you can see how they compare and have an idea about when to use them. Statisticians use nonparametric analyses much less frequently than their parametric counterparts.

Hypothesis Testing

Hypothesis testing is a statistical analysis that uses sample data to assess two mutually exclusive theories about the properties of a population. Statisticians call these theories the null hypothesis and the alternative hypothesis. A hypothesis test assesses your sample statistic and factors in an estimate of the sampling error to determine which hypothesis the data support.

When you can reject the null hypothesis, the results are statistically significant, and your data support the theory that an effect exists at the population level.

Hypothesis tests use sample data to answer questions like the following:

- Is the population mean greater than or less than a particular value?
- Are the means of two or more populations different from each other?

For example, if we study the effectiveness of a new medication by comparing the outcomes in a treatment and control group, hypothesis tests can tell us whether the drug's effect that we observe in the sample is likely to exist in the population. After all, we don't want to use the medication if it is effective only in our specific sample. Instead, we need evidence that it'll be useful in the entire population of patients. Hypothesis tests allow us to draw these types of conclusions about whole populations.

Null Hypothesis

In hypothesis testing, the null hypothesis is one of two mutually exclusive theories about the population's properties. Typically, the null hypothesis states there is no effect (i.e., the effect size equals zero). H_0 often signifies the null.

In all hypothesis testing, the researchers are testing an effect of some sort. Effects can be the effectiveness of a new vaccination, the durability of a new product, the proportion of defects in a manufacturing process, and so on. There is some benefit or difference that the researchers hope to identify.

However, there might be no effect or no difference between the experimental groups. In statistics, we call this lack of an effect the null hypothesis. Therefore, if you can reject the null, you can favor the alternative hypothesis, which states that the effect exists (doesn't equal zero) at the population level.

You can think of the null as the default theory that requires sufficiently strong evidence in your sample to be able to reject it.

For example, when you're comparing the means of two groups, the null often states that the difference between the two means equals zero. In other words, the groups are not different.

Alternative Hypothesis

The alternative hypothesis is the other theory about the properties of the population in hypothesis testing. Typically, the alternative hypothesis states that a population parameter does not equal the null hypothesis value. In other words, there is a non-zero effect. If your sample contains sufficient evidence, you can reject the null and favor the alternative hypothesis. H_1 or H_A usually identifies the alternative.

For example, if you're comparing the means of two groups, the alternative hypothesis often states that the difference between the two means does not equal zero.

The null and alternative hypotheses are always mutually exclusive.

Effect

The effect is the difference between the population value and the null hypothesis value. The effect is also known as population effect or the difference. For example, the mean difference between the health outcome for a treatment group and a control group is the effect.

Typically, you do not know the size of the actual effect. However, you can use a hypothesis test to determine whether an effect exists and estimate its size.

For example, if the mean of one group is 10 and the mean of another group is 2, the effect is 8.

Significance Level (Alpha)

The significance level defines how strong the sample evidence must be to conclude an effect exists in the population.

The significance level, also known as alpha or α, is an evidentiary standard that researchers set before the study. It specifies how strongly the sample evidence must contradict the null hypothesis before you can reject the null for the entire population. This standard is defined by the probability of rejecting a true null hypothesis. In other words, it is the probability that you say there is an effect when there is no effect. Lower significance levels indicate that you require more substantial evidence before you will reject the null.

For instance, a significance level of 0.05 signifies a 5% risk of deciding that an effect exists when it does not exist.

Use p-values and significance levels together to determine which hypothesis the data support, as described in the p-value section.

P-values

P-values indicate the strength of the sample evidence against the null hypothesis. If it is less than the significance level, your results are statistically significant.

P-values are the probability that you would obtain the effect observed in your sample, or larger, if the null hypothesis is correct. In simpler terms, p-values tell you how strongly your sample data contradict the null. Lower p-values represent stronger evidence against the null.

If the p-value is less than or equal to the significance level, you reject the null hypothesis and your results are statistically significant. The data support the alternative hypothesis that the effect exists in the population. When the p-value is greater than the significance level, your sample data don't provide enough evidence to conclude that the effect exists.

Here's the statistical terminology for these decisions.

- When the p-value is less than or equal to the significance level, you reject the null hypothesis.
- When the p-value is greater than the significance level, you fail to reject the null hypothesis.

If you need help remembering this rule about comparing p-values to significance levels, here are two mnemonic phrases:

- When the p-value is low, the null must go.
- If the p-value is high, the null will fly.

Statistical Significance

When your p-value is less than the significance level, your results are statistically significant. This condition indicates the strength of the evidence in your sample (p-value) exceeds the evidentiary standard you defined (significance level). Your sample evidence provides sufficient evidence to conclude that the effect exists in the population.

Confidence intervals (CIs)

In inferential statistics, a principal goal is to estimate population parameters. These parameters are the unknown values for the entire population, such as the population mean and standard deviation.

Typically, it's impossible to measure an entire population. Consequently, parameter values are not only unknown but almost always unknowable. The sampling error I mentioned earlier produces uncertainty, or a margin of error, around our parameter estimates.

Suppose we define our population as all high school basketball players. Then, we draw a random sample from this population and calculate the mean height of 181 cm. This sample estimate of 181 cm is the best estimate of the mean height of the population. Because the mean is from a sample, it's virtually guaranteed that our estimate of the population parameter is not exactly correct.

Confidence intervals incorporate the uncertainty and sample error to create a range of values the actual population value is likely to fall within. For example, a confidence interval of [176 186] indicates that we can be confident that the real population mean falls within this range.

Significance Levels In-Depth

Before getting to the first example of a hypothesis test, I want you to understand significance levels conceptually. It lies at the heart of how we use statistics to learn. How do we determine that we have significant results?

Significance levels in statistics are a crucial component of hypothesis testing. However, unlike other values in your statistical output, the significance level is not something that statistical software calculates. Instead, you choose the significance level. Why is that?

e.2. Set the α at 5%.

In this section, I'll explain the significance level, why you choose its value, and how to choose a good value.

Your sample data provide evidence for an effect. The significance level is a measure of how strong the sample evidence must be before determining the results are statistically significant. It defines the line between the evidence being strong enough to conclude that the effect exists in the population versus it's weak enough that we can't rule out the possibility that the sample effect is just random sampling error. Because we're talking about evidence, let's look at a courtroom analogy.

Evidentiary Standards in the Courtroom

Criminal cases and civil cases vary greatly, but both require a minimum amount of evidence to convince a judge or jury to prove a claim against the defendant. Prosecutors in criminal cases must prove the defendant is guilty "beyond a reasonable doubt," whereas plaintiffs in a civil case must present a "preponderance of the evidence." These terms are evidentiary standards that reflect the amount of evidence that civil and criminal cases require.

For civil cases, most scholars define a preponderance of evidence as meaning that at least 51% of the evidence shown supports the plaintiff's claim. However, criminal cases are more severe and require more substantial evidence, which must go beyond a reasonable doubt. Most scholars define that evidentiary standard as being 90%, 95%, or even 99% sure that the defendant is guilty.

In statistics, the significance level is the evidentiary standard. For researchers to successfully make the case that the effect exists in the population, the sample must contain sufficient evidence.

In court cases, you have evidentiary standards because you don't want to convict innocent people.

In hypothesis tests, we have the significance level because we don't want to claim that an effect or relationship exists when it does not exist.

Significance Levels as an Evidentiary Standard

In statistics, the significance level defines the strength of evidence in probabilistic terms. Specifically, alpha represents the probability that tests will produce statistically significant results when the null hypothesis is correct. You can think of this error rate as the probability of a false positive. The test results lead you to believe that an effect exists when it actually does not exist.

Obviously, when the null hypothesis is correct, we want a low probability that hypothesis tests will produce statistically significant results. For example, if alpha is 0.05, your analysis has a 5% chance of a significant outcome when the null hypothesis is correct.

Just as the evidentiary standard varies by the type of court case, you can set the significance level for a hypothesis test depending on the consequences of a false positive. By changing alpha, you increase or decrease the amount of evidence you require in the sample to conclude that the effect exists in the population.

Changing Significance Levels

Because 0.05 is the standard alpha, we'll start by adjusting away from that value. Typically, you'll need a good reason to change the significance level to something other than 0.05. Also, note the inverse relationship between alpha and the amount of required evidence. For instance, increasing the significance level from 0.05 to 0.10 lowers the evidentiary standard. Conversely, decreasing it from 0.05 to 0.01 increases the bar. Let's look at why you would consider changing alpha and how it affects your hypothesis test.

Increasing the Significance Level

Imagine you're testing the strength of party balloons. You'll use the test results to determine which brand of balloons to buy. A false positive here leads you to buy balloons that are not stronger. The drawbacks of a false positive are very low. Consequently, you could consider lessening the amount of evidence required by changing the significance level to 0.10. Because this change decreases the amount of evidence needed, it makes your test more sensitive to detecting differences, but it also increases the chance of a false positive from 5% to 10%.

Decreasing the Significance Level

Conversely, imagine you're testing the strength of fabric for hot air balloons. A false positive here is very risky because lives are on the line! You want to be very confident that the material from one manufacturer is stronger than the other. In this case, you should increase the amount of evidence required by changing alpha to 0.01. Because this change increases the amount of evidence needed, it makes your test less sensitive to detecting differences, but it decreases the chance of a false positive from 5% to 1%.

It's all about the tradeoff between sensitivity and false positives!

In conclusion, a significance level of 0.05 is the most common. However, it's the analyst's responsibility to determine how much evidence to require for concluding that an effect exists. How problematic is a false positive? There is no single correct answer for all circumstances. Consequently, you need to choose the significance level!

While significance levels indicate the amount of evidence required, p-values represent the strength of the evidence in your sample. When your p-value is less than or equal to the significance level, the strength of the sample evidence meets or exceeds your evidentiary standard for rejecting the null hypothesis and concluding that the effect exists.

How Hypothesis Tests Work

Here's the approach I'll use throughout the book. I'll start with this example that compares a sample mean to a target value. It's an excellent place to start because it's a relatively simple test. I'll intentionally gloss over some of the finer details for now so you can focus on the basics of why you use this test, how it works in a general sense, and how to interpret the results.

In later chapters, I'll add in more of the details and considerations that we're skipping here. At first, I'll stick mainly with hypothesis tests that compare group means because they are the most common. After covering the basics of tests for means, you'll understand the fundamental mechanics for all hypothesis tests. At that point, I'll switch to other types of hypothesis tests and help you determine which ones to use for your data.

Hypothesis testing is a vital process in inferential statistics where the goal is to use sample data to draw conclusions about an entire population. In the testing process, you use significance levels and p-values to determine whether the test results are statistically significant. In this section, I'll keep the discussion more general to avoid using terminology that we haven't covered yet, although you will learn about one new concept—sampling distributions.

You hear about results being statistically significant all the time. But, what do significance levels, p-values, and statistical significance actually represent? Why do we even need to use hypothesis tests in statistics?

I'll answer all of these questions using graphs and concepts to explain how hypothesis tests function to provide a more intuitive explanation.

Let's start by understanding why we need to use hypothesis tests.

A researcher is studying fuel expenditures for families and wants to determine if the monthly cost had changed since last year when the average was $260 per month. The researcher draws a random sample of 25 families and analyzes their monthly costs for this year. To follow along, use the CSV data file: FuelCosts. Below are the descriptive statistics for this year.

```
Descriptive Statistics: Fuel Cost

             Total
Variable    Count   Mean   SE Mean   StDev
Fuel Cost      25  330.6      30.8   154.2
```

We'll build on this example to answer the research question and show how hypothesis tests work.

Descriptive Statistics Won't Answer the Question

The researcher collected a random sample and found that this year's sample mean (330.6) is greater than last year's mean (260). Why perform a hypothesis test at all? We can see that this year's mean is higher by $70! Isn't that different?

Regrettably, the situation isn't as straightforward as you might think because we're analyzing a sample instead of the full population. There are huge benefits when working with samples because it is usually impossible to collect data from an entire population. However, the tradeoff for working with a manageable sample requires that we account for sample error.

The sampling error is the gap between the sample statistic and the population parameter. For our example, the sample statistic is the sample mean, which is 330.6. The population parameter is μ, or mu, which is the average of the entire population. Unfortunately, the value of the population parameter is unknowable.

We obtained a sample mean of 330.6. However, it's conceivable that, due to sampling error, the mean of the population might be only 260. If the researcher drew another random sample, the next sample mean might be closer to 260. It's impossible to assess this possibility by looking at only the sample mean.

We need to use a hypothesis test to determine the likelihood of obtaining our sample mean if the population mean is 260.

A Sampling Distribution Determines Whether Our Sample Mean is Unlikely

It is improbable for any sample mean to equal the population mean because of sample error. In our case, the sample mean of 330.6 is almost definitely not equal to the population mean for fuel expenditures.

If we could obtain a substantial number of random samples and calculate the sample mean for each sample, we'd observe a broad spectrum of sample means. We'd even be able to graph the distribution of sample means from this process.

This type of distribution is called a sampling distribution. You obtain a sampling distribution by drawing many random samples of the same size from the same population. Why the heck would we do this?

Because sampling distributions allow you to determine the likelihood of obtaining your sample statistic and they're crucial for performing hypothesis tests.

Luckily, we don't need to go to the trouble of collecting numerous random samples! Statistical procedures estimate sampling distributions using the properties of samples. In chapter 3, I'll show this process in-depth. For now, I want you to focus on the idea that the one sample the study collected is only one of an infinite number of potential samples it could have drawn. That's a crucial concept in hypothesis testing and inferential statistics.

We want to find out if the average fuel expenditure this year (330.6) is different from last year (260). To answer this question, we'll graph the sampling distribution based on the assumption that the mean fuel cost for the entire population has not changed and is still 260. Hypothesis tests always use sampling distributions that assume the null hypothesis is correct. Likewise, we use the null hypothesis value as the basis of comparison for our observed sample value.

Graphing our Sample Mean in the Context of the Sampling Distribution

The graph below shows which sample means are more likely and less likely if the population mean is 260. We can place our sample mean in this distribution. This broader context helps us see how unlikely our sample mean is if the null hypothesis is correct ($\mu = 260$).

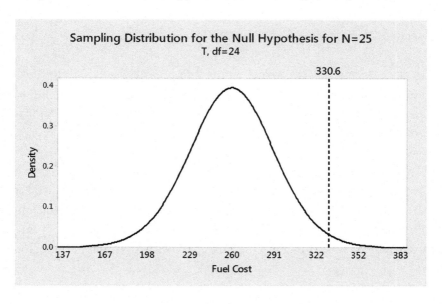

The graph displays the estimated distribution of sample means. The most likely values are near 260 because the plot assumes that the null hypothesis value is the real population mean. However, given random sampling error, it would not be surprising to observe sample means ranging from 167 to 352. If the population mean is still 260, our observed sample mean (330.6) isn't the most likely value, but it's not entirely implausible either.

Sampling distributions are a type of probability distribution plot, which I discuss in more detail in my *Introduction to Statistics* book. On a probability plot, the entire area under the distribution curve equals 1. The proportion of the area under a curve that corresponds to a range of values along the X-axis represents the likelihood a value will fall within that range. Hypothesis tests use the ability of probability distributions to calculate probabilities for ranges of values to determine statistical significance.

The sampling distribution indicates that we are relatively unlikely to obtain a sample of 330.6 if the population mean is 260. Is our sample mean *so* unlikely that we can reject the notion that the population mean is 260?

In statistics, we call this rejecting the null hypothesis. If we reject the null for our example, the difference between the sample mean (330.6) and 260 is statistically significant. In other words, the sample data favor the hypothesis that the population average does *not* equal 260.

However, look at the sampling distribution chart again. Notice that there is no particular location on the curve where you can definitively draw this conclusion. There is only a consistent decrease in the likelihood of observing sample means that are farther from the null hypothesis value. Where do we decide a sample mean is far away enough?

To answer this question, we'll need more hypothesis testing tools! The hypothesis testing procedure quantifies our sample's unusualness with a probability and then compares it to an evidentiary standard. This process allows you to make an objective decision about the strength of the evidence.

We're going to add the tools we need to make this decision to the graph—significance levels and p-values!

These tools allow us to test these two hypotheses:

- Null hypothesis: The population mean equals the null hypothesis mean (260).
- Alternative hypothesis: The population mean does not equal the null hypothesis mean (260).

Graphing Significance Levels as Critical Regions

As we covered earlier in this chapter, the significance level is an evidentiary standard that a researcher sets before the study. It defines how strongly the sample evidence must contradict the null hypothesis before you can reject the null hypothesis for the entire population. The strength of the evidence is determined by the probability of rejecting a true null hypothesis.

Lower significance levels require stronger sample evidence to be able to reject the null hypothesis. For example, to be statistically significant at the 0.01 significance level requires more substantial evidence than the 0.05 significance level.

The technical nature of these types of questions can make your head spin. A picture can bring these ideas to life!

On the probability distribution plot, the significance level defines how far the sample value must be from the null value before we can reject the null hypothesis. The percentage of the area under the curve that is shaded equals the probability that the sample value will fall in those regions if the null hypothesis is correct.

To represent a significance level of 0.05, I'll shade 5% of the distribution furthest from the null value.

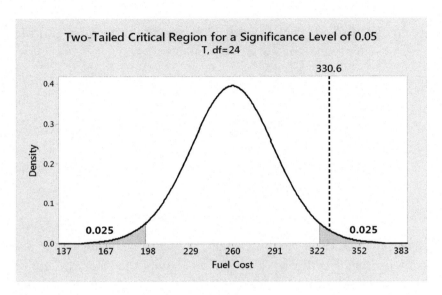

The two shaded regions in the graph are equidistant from the central value of the null hypothesis. Each region has a probability of 0.025, which sums to our desired total of 0.05. These shaded areas are called the critical regions for a two-tailed hypothesis test.

The critical region defines sample values that are improbable enough to warrant rejecting the null hypothesis. If the null hypothesis is correct and the population mean is 260, random samples (n=25) from this population have means that fall in the critical regions 5% of the time.

Our sample mean is statistically significant at the 0.05 level because it falls in the critical region.

What Are P-values?

P-values are the probability that a sample will have an effect at least as extreme as the effect observed in your sample *if* the null hypothesis is correct.

This tortuous, technical definition for p-values can make your head spin. Let's graph it!

First, we need to calculate the effect that is present in our sample. The effect is the distance between the sample value and the null value: 330.6 − 260 = 70.6. Next, I'll shade the regions on both sides of the distribution that are at least as far away as 70.6 from the null (260 +/- 70.6). This process graphs the probability of observing a sample mean at least as extreme as our sample mean.

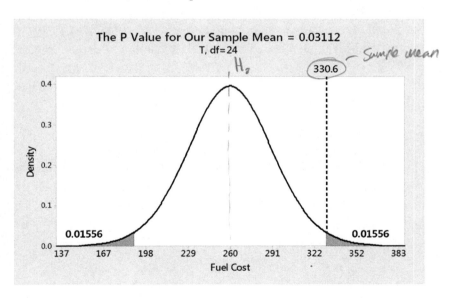

The total probability of the two shaded regions is 0.03112. If the null hypothesis value (260) is true and you drew many random samples, you'd expect sample means to fall in the shaded regions about 3.1% of the time. In other words, you will observe sample effects at least as large as 70.6 about 3.1% of the time if the null hypothesis is correct. That's the p-value!

There's a reason why I'm shading both tails. We'll come back to this in chapter 6 when compare one-tailed and two-tailed tests!

Using P-values and Significance Levels Together

If your p-value is less than or equal to your alpha level, reject the null hypothesis.

The p-value results are consistent with our graphical representation. The p-value of 0.03112 is significant at the alpha level of 0.05.

With a significance level of 0.05, the sample effect is statistically significant. Our data support the alternative hypothesis, which states that the population mean doesn't equal 260. We can conclude that mean fuel expenditures have increased since last year.

Chapter 4 discusses the proper interpretation of p-values in much more detail.

Discussion about Statistically Significant Results

Hypothesis tests determine whether your sample data provide evidence that is strong enough to reject the null hypothesis for the entire population. The test compares your sample statistic to the null value and determines whether it is sufficiently rare. "Sufficiently rare" is defined in a hypothesis test by:

- Assuming that the null hypothesis is correct—the graphs center on the null value.
- The significance (alpha) level—how far out from the null value is the critical region?
- The sample statistic—is it within the critical region?

There is no special significance level that correctly determines which studies have real population effects 100% of the time. The traditional significance levels of 0.05 and 0.01 are attempts to manage the tradeoff between having a low probability of rejecting a true null hypothesis and detecting an effect if one actually exists.

The significance level is the rate at which you incorrectly reject null hypotheses that are actually true. For example, for all studies that use a significance level of 0.05 and the null hypothesis is correct, you can expect 5% of them to have sample statistics that fall in the critical region. When this error occurs, you aren't aware that the null hypothesis is correct, but you'll reject it because the p-value is less than 0.05.

This error does not indicate that the researcher made a mistake. As the graphs show, you can observe extreme sample statistics due to sample error alone. It's the luck of the draw!

Hypothesis tests are crucial when you want to use sample data to make conclusions about a population because these tests account for sample error. Using significance levels and p-values to determine when to reject the null hypothesis improves the probability that you will draw the correct conclusion.

How Confidence Intervals Work

A confidence interval is calculated from a sample and provides a range of values that likely contains the unknown value of a population parameter. In this section, I demonstrate how confidence intervals and confidence levels work using graphs and concepts. In the process, you'll see how confidence intervals are very similar to p-values and significance levels.

You can calculate a confidence interval from a sample to obtain a range for where the population parameter is likely to reside. For example, a confidence interval of [9 11] indicates that the population mean is likely to be between 9 and 11.

Different random samples drawn from the same population are liable to produce slightly different intervals. If you draw many random samples and calculate a confidence interval for each sample, a specific proportion of the intervals contain the population parameter. That percentage is the confidence level.

For example, a 95% confidence level suggests that if you draw 20 random samples from the same population, you'd expect 19 of the confidence intervals to include the population value, as shown below. The one highlighted interval does not contain the population value, which the dashed line represents.

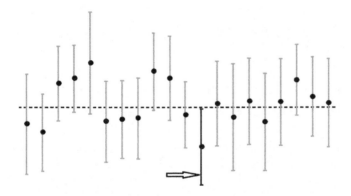

The confidence interval procedure provides meaningful estimates because it produces ranges that usually contain the parameter.

We'll create a confidence interval for the population mean using the fuel cost example that we've been developing. With other types of data, you can create intervals for proportions, frequencies, regression coefficients, and differences between populations.

Precision of the Estimate

Confidence intervals include the point estimate for the sample with a margin of error around the point estimate. The point estimate is the most likely value of the parameter and equals the sample value. The margin of error accounts for the amount of doubt involved in estimating the population parameter. The more variability there is in the sample data, the less precise the estimate, which causes the margin of error to extend further out from the point estimate. Confidence intervals help you navigate the uncertainty of how well a sample estimates a value for an entire population.

With this in mind, confidence intervals can help you compare the precision of different estimates. Suppose two studies estimate the same mean of 10. It appears like they obtained the same results. However, using 95% confidence intervals, we see that one interval is [5 15] while the other is [9 11]. The latter confidence interval is narrower, which suggests that it is a more precise estimate.

Graphical Representation

Let's delve into how confidence intervals incorporate the margin of error. Like the previous sections, I'll use the same sampling distribution that showed us how hypothesis tests work.

There are two critical differences between the sampling distribution graphs for significance levels and confidence intervals. The significance level chart centers on the null value, and we shade the outside 5% of the distribution. Conversely, the confidence interval graph centers on the sample mean, and we shade the center 95% of the distribution.

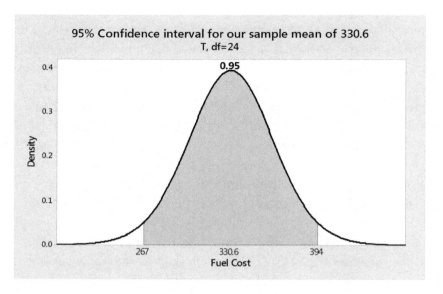

The shaded range of sample means [267 392] covers 95% of this sampling distribution. This range is the 95% confidence interval for our sample data. We can be 95% confident that the population mean for fuel costs fall between 267 and 392.

The graph emphasizes the role of uncertainty around the point estimate. This graph centers on our sample mean. If the population mean equals our sample mean, random samples (N=25) from this population will fall within this range 95% of the time.

We don't really know whether our sample mean is near the population mean. However, we know that the sample mean is an unbiased estimate of the population mean. An unbiased estimate is one that doesn't tend to be too high or too low. It's correct on average. Confidence intervals are correct on average because they use sample estimates that are correct on average. Given what we know, the sample mean is the most likely value for the population mean.

Given the sampling distribution, it would not be unusual for other random samples drawn from the same population to have means that fall within the shaded area. In other words, given that we did obtain the sample mean of 330.6, it would not be surprising to get other sample means within the shaded range.

If these other sample means would not be unusual, then we must conclude that these other values are also likely candidates for the population mean. There is inherent uncertainty when you use sample data to make inferences about an entire population. Confidence intervals help you gauge the amount of uncertainty in your sample estimates.

Confidence Intervals and P-values Always Agree

If you want to determine whether your test results are statistically significant, you can use either p-values with significance levels or confidence intervals. These two approaches always agree.

The relationship between the confidence level and the significance level for a hypothesis test is as follows:

Confidence level = 1 − Significance level (alpha)

For example, if your significance level is 0.05, the equivalent confidence level is 95%.

Both of the following conditions represent a hypothesis test with statistically significant results:

- The p-value is smaller than the significance level.
- The confidence interval excludes the null hypothesis value.

Further, it is always true that when the p-value is less than your significance level, the interval excludes the value of the null hypothesis.

In the fuel cost example, our hypothesis test results are statistically significant because the p-value (0.03112) is less than the significance level (0.05). Likewise, the 95% confidence interval [267 394] excludes the null hypothesis value (260). Using either method, we draw the same conclusion.

The p-value and confidence interval results always agree. To understand the basis of this agreement, we need to remember how confidence levels and significance levels function:

- A confidence level determines the distance between the sample mean and the confidence limits.
- A significance level determines the distance between the null hypothesis value and the critical regions.

Both concepts specify a distance from the mean to a limit. Surprise! These distances are precisely the same length.

The hypothesis test in this example is a 1-sample t-test, which calculates this distance as follows:

The critical t-value * standard error of the mean

Interpreting these statistics goes beyond the scope of this section. But, using this equation, the distance for our fuel cost example is $63.57.

P-value and significance level approach: If the sample mean is more than $63.57 from the null hypothesis mean, the sample mean falls within a critical region, and the difference is statistically significant.

Confidence interval approach: If the null hypothesis mean is more than $63.57 from the sample mean, the interval does not contain this value, and the difference is statistically significant.

Of course, they always agree!

When the same hypothesis test generates the p-values and confidence intervals, and you use an equivalent confidence level and significance level, the two approaches always agree.

I Really Like Confidence Intervals!

Analysts often place more emphasis on using p-values to determine whether a result is statistically significant. Unfortunately, a statistically significant effect might not always be practically meaningful. For example, a significant effect can be too small to be of any importance in the real world.

You should always consider both the size and precision of the estimated effect. Ideally, an estimated effect is both large enough to be meaningful and sufficiently precise for you to trust. Confidence intervals allow you to assess both of these considerations!

Review and Next Steps

This chapter covered the essential differences between descriptive and inferential statistics. If you want to generalize your results beyond a sample to a larger population, you'll need to use a representative sampling methodology and a test that factors in sampling error. You don't want to confuse sampling error with a real effect! Hypothesis tests help you make the correct decisions.

After covering some basic terminology and concepts, I presented a simplified version of a hypothesis test. In this example, I introduced the concept of a sampling distribution. Hypothesis testing treats the sample that a study collects as only one of an infinite number that the study could have collected. By constructing a sampling distribution that assumes the null hypothesis is correct, we can determine how unusual our data are if the null is true.

While the hypothesis test in this chapter was unnamed, it is a 1-sample t-test because it compared a single sample mean to a target value. Chapter 2 explores t-tests in more detail. You'll learn about the different types of t-tests and when to use each one, the assumptions and conditions that your data must satisfy to produce reliable results, and how to interpret these t-tests.

T-Test Uses, Assumptions, and Analyses

The example in the previous chapter used a 1-sample t-test. In this chapter, we'll explore t-tests in greater detail. I want you to get your feet wet quickly and know how to interpret the statistical output for t-tests. Then, we'll dive into a deeper understanding of how t-tests work behind the scenes.

T-tests are hypothesis tests that assess the means of one or two groups. Depending on the t-test and how you configure it, the test can determine whether:

- One mean is different from a hypothesized value.
- Two group means are different.
- Paired means are different.

In this chapter, you will learn about three t-tests, 1-sample t-tests, 2-sample tests, and paired t-tests. When statisticians talk about one-sample and two-sample tests, we're referring to how many groups we're comparing. One-sample tests have one group and the test compares the group mean to a target value. That was the type of test in the energy cost example. Two-sample tests compare two groups. Are the means equal or different?

t-Tests can compare the means for up to two groups. If you have three or more groups, you'll need to use ANOVA. That's a topic for a later chapter!

Before we get to the t-tests themselves, we need to talk about their assumptions. In statistics, if you do not satisfy the assumptions for a particular procedure, you might not be able to trust the results.

In chapter 1, we talked about one assumption. We saw how inferential statistics and hypothesis tests require unbiased, representative samples. If you use a sampling methodology that produces a non-representative sample, you can't trust your hypothesis test results. The underlying data just don't represent the population you're studying. However, there are other assumptions you need to consider. All hypothesis tests have some assumptions. Many are similar between tests, but some are unique to particular methods.

Before getting to the tests, I need to make an essential point about graphing your data. As I discuss in my *Introduction to Statistics* book, data analysis is best when you use graphs and numeric analysis together. Charts bring your data to life in a way that statistical output cannot. Additionally, they are an easy way to identify potential problems, such as skewed distributions and outliers. While graphing is a crucial part of the process, I focus on the hypothesis tests themselves in this book.

1-Sample t-Tests

Use a one-sample t-test to compare your sample mean to a hypothesized value for the population and to create a confidence interval of likely values for the population mean. Typically, researchers use a hypothesized value that is meaningful for their study, which forms the null hypothesis for the test.

Please note that with a 1-sample t-test, you don't need to perform the hypothesis test. If you just want to understand the precision of the estimate, assess the confidence interval to identify the range of likely values. That information can be valuable even when you don't have a reference or hypothesized value.

In the energy cost example, researchers compared the current year's mean cost to last year's mean cost. The researchers used the sample data for the current year and entered the previous year's mean cost for the hypothesized value.

The 1-sample t-test has the following hypotheses:

- **Null**: The population mean equals the hypothesized mean.
- **Alternative**: The population mean does not equal the hypothesized mean.

If the p-value is less than your significance level (e.g., 0.05), you can reject the null hypothesis. The difference between the sample mean and the hypothesized mean is statistically significant. Your sample provides strong enough evidence to conclude that the population mean does not equal the hypothesized mean.

Assumptions

The assumptions for the 1-sample t-test cover a variety of issues that range from data collection, data type, and properties of the data. For reliable 1-sample t-test results, your data should satisfy the following assumptions:

You have a random sample

Drawing a random sample from the population you are studying helps ensure that your data represent the population. Representative samples are vital when you want to make inferences about the population. If your data do not represent the population, your analysis results will not be valid for that population.

You must draw a random sample from your population of interest. Each item or person in the population must have an equal probability of being selected.

For example, if you're studying demographic information in a city and randomly approach people in a mall, the people probably do not accurately represent the entire state. People in that specific mall are likely to live within a particular geographic region and have distinct socio-economic characteristics that don't represent the city's population.

Your data must be continuous

T-tests require continuous data. Continuous variables can take on any numeric value, and the scale can be meaningfully divided into smaller increments, including fractional and decimal values. There are an infinite number of possible values between any two values. And the difference between any two values is always meaningful. Typically, you measure continuous variables on a scale. For example, when you measure height, weight, and temperature, you have continuous data.

Other hypothesis tests can analyze different types of data. I'll cover those in later chapters.

Your sample data should follow a normal distribution or have more than 20 observations

T-tests assume that your data follow the normal distribution, which many natural phenomena follow. The normal distribution is that familiar symmetric, bell-shaped curve in statistics. However, when your sample is larger than 20, your data can be skewed and the test results will still be reliable. When your sample size is less than 20, graph your data and determine whether the distribution is skewed or has outliers. Either of these conditions can cause the test results to be unreliable.

Fortunately, if you have more than 20 observations, you don't have to worry about the normality assumption in most cases. In chapter 7, I discuss how the central limit theorem allows you to waive the normality assumption when your sample size is sufficiently large.

1-sample t-test example

Imagine we've conducted a simple experiment using a random sample of participants. We want to determine whether the participants have mastered a skill more than a target value after attending an educational session. After the session, we assess the skill level of 15 participants using a validated assessment.

We want to determine whether the mean score of these participants is different than the reference value of 60. A significantly higher mean represents an improvement. To try this yourself, use the CSV data file: Assessment Scores.

One-Sample T: Score

Test of $\mu = 60$ vs $\neq 60$

Variable	N	Mean	StDev	SE Mean	95% CI	T	P
Fuel Cost	15	64.16	11.35	2.93	(57.87, 70.45)	1.42	0.178

Let's analyze the data!

The output indicates that the mean score is 64.16, which is higher than the reference value. For now, the p-value is the most important statistic. We'll learn about t-values and degrees of freedom in later chapters.

If the p-value is less than your significance level, the difference between the mean and reference value is statistically significant.

Because our p-value (0.178) is greater than the standard significance level of 0.05, we fail to reject the null hypothesis. If the p-value is high, the null will fly! Our sample data do not provide enough evidence to support the claim that the population mean is different from 60. We cannot conclude that the educational session was useful.

Furthermore, the sample estimate of the mean (64.16) is based on 15 observations and is unlikely to equal the population mean. The confidence interval estimates that the actual population mean is likely between 57.87 and 70.45. The confidence interval includes the reference value of 60, which is why we cannot conclude that the population mean is different from that value.

Later in this chapter, I discuss in detail what it means when we fail to reject the null hypothesis and why statisticians don't accept the null. For now, just know that we don't have enough evidence to conclude that the population mean is different from 60. However, this result doesn't prove that the population mean equals 60.

2-Sample t-Tests

Use two-sample t-tests to compare the means of precisely two groups—no more and no less! The procedure also creates a confidence interval of the mean difference. Typically, you perform this test to determine whether two population means are different.

For example, do students who learn using Method A have a different mean score than those who learn using Method B?

2-sample t-tests have the following hypotheses:

- **Null hypothesis:** The means for the two populations are equal.
- **Alternative hypothesis:** The means for the two populations are not equal.

If the p-value is less than your significance level (e.g., 0.05), you can reject the null hypothesis. The difference between the two means is statistically significant. Your sample provides strong enough evidence to conclude that the two population means are not equal.

Assumptions

The assumptions for 2-sample t-tests are similar to those for the 1-sample version. I'll focus on the differences below.

For reliable 2-sample t-test results, your data should satisfy the following assumptions:
- You have a representative, random sample
- Your data must be continuous

However, there are several differences between the 1-sample and 2-sample t-tests.

Your sample data should follow a normal distribution or each group has more than 15 observations

All t-tests assume that your data follow the distribution. However, as you saw for 1-sample t-tests, you can waive this assumption if your sample size is large enough.

For the 2-sample t-test, when each group is larger than 15, your data can be skewed and the test results will still be reliable. When your sample size is less than 15 per group, graph your data and determine whether the two distributions are skewed or has outliers. Either of these conditions can cause the test results to be unreliable.

Fortunately, if you have more than 15 observations in each group, you don't have to worry about the normality assumption too much.

The groups are independent

Independent samples contain different sets of items in each sample. 2-sample t-tests compare measurements taken on two distinct groups. If you have the same people or items in both groups, you can use the paired t-test.

Groups can have equal or unequal variances but use the correct form of the test

Variance, and the closely related standard deviation, are measures of variability. Each group in your analysis has its own variance. The two-sample t-test has two methods. One method assumes that the two groups have equal variances while the other does not assume they are equal. The form that does not assume equal variances is known as Welch's t-test.

When the sample sizes for both groups are equal, or nearly equal, and you have a moderate sample size, t-tests are robust to differences between variances. If one group has twice the variance of another group, it's time to use Welch's t-test! However, you don't need to worry about smaller differences.

If you have unequal variances *and* unequal sample sizes, it's vital to use the unequal variances version of the 2-sample t-test!

2-sample t-test example

Let's conduct a two-sample t-test! Our hypothetical scenario is that we are comparing scores from two teaching methods. We drew two random samples of students. Students in one group learned using Method A while the other group used Method B. These samples contain entirely separate students.

Now, we want to determine whether the two means are different. To perform these t-tests, use the CSV file that contains all data for the 2-sample t-test and the paired t-test examples: t-TestExamples.

Here is what the data look like in the datasheet.

Method A	Method B
72.471714	72.145335
72.100548	89.811362
69.700219	98.071997
61.294691	84.486978
76.509736	80.530738
81.288642	84.8586
75.898287	70.828394
71.610303	90.863795
82.005608	73.113933
52.743031	93.715501
64.720142	83.399928
89.807999	86.025116
74.101	92.191169
60.052173	91.876728
68.25018	79.216534

Let's assume that the variances are equal and use the Assuming Equal Variances version.

Two-Sample T-Test and CI: Method A, Method B

```
Two-sample T for Method A vs Method B

          N  Mean   StDev  SE Mean
Method A  15 71.50   9.41    2.4  ) close enough
Method B  15 84.74   8.31    2.1

Difference = μ (Method A) - μ (Method B)
Estimate for difference:  -13.24
95% CI for difference:  (-19.89, -6.59)
T-Test of difference = 0 (vs ≠): T-Value = -4.08 P-Value = 0.000
```

The output indicates that the mean for Method A is 71.50 and for Method B it is 84.74. Looking in the Standard Deviation column, we can see that they are not exactly equal, but they are close enough to assume equal variances.

Because our p-value (0.000) is less than the standard significance level of 0.05, we can reject the null hypothesis. If the p-value is low, the null must go! Our sample data support the claim that the population means are different. Specifically, Method B's mean is greater than Method A's mean. If high scores are better, then Method B is significantly better than Method A.

The sample estimate of the mean difference is -13.24. However, that estimate is based on 30 observations split between the two groups and it is unlikely to equal the population difference. The confidence interval estimates that the mean difference between these two methods for the entire population is likely between -19.89 and -6.59.

The negative values reflect the fact that Method A has a lower mean than Method B (i.e., Method A − Method B < 0). The confidence interval excludes the value of zero (no difference between groups), so we can conclude that the population means are different.

Paired t-Tests

Use paired t-tests to assess dependent samples, which are two measurements on the same person or item.

Suppose you gather a random sample of people. You give them all a
pretest, administer a treatment, and then perform a posttest. Each subject has a pretest and posttest score. Or, perhaps you have a sample of
wood boards, and you paint half of each board with one paint and the
other half with different paint. Then, you measure the paint durability
for both types of paint on all the boards. Each board has two paint
durability scores.

In both cases, you can use a paired t-test to determine whether the
difference between the means of the two sets of scores is statistically
significant.

Assumptions

For reliable paired t-test results, your data should satisfy the following
assumptions:

- You have a representative, random sample
- Your sample contains independent observations
- Your data must be continuous
- Data should follow a normal distribution or have a sample size
  larger than 20.

Dependent Samples

Unlike 2-sample t-tests, paired t-tests use the same people or items in
both groups. One way to determine whether a paired t-test is appropriate for your data is if each row in the dataset corresponds to one
person or item.

Paired t-Test example

For this example, imagine that we have a training program. We need to determine whether the difference between the mean pretest score and the mean post-test score is significantly different.

Here is what the data look like in the datasheet. Note that the analysis does not use the subject's ID number.

SubjectID	Pretest	Posttest
1	90.56295	110.642
2	94.81579	101.588
3	109.5623	120.6072
4	90.22167	83.22168
5	97.59779	109.2724
6	91.16687	115.8063
7	96.64992	99.89581
8	97.61626	117.9404
9	88.84491	106.0523
10	90.81701	82.82288
11	89.29369	116.6393
12	115.8319	128.6098
13	121.2873	119.6646
14	87.87179	108.383
15	93.79326	96.37379

Paired T-Test and CI: Pretest, Posttest

```
Paired T for Pretest - Posttest

                N    Mean   StDev   SE Mean
Pretest        15   97.06   10.31     2.66
Posttest       15  107.83   13.25     3.42
Difference     15  -10.77   11.17     2.88

95% CI for mean difference: (-16.96, -4.59)
T-Test of mean difference = 0 (vs ≠ 0):
T-value = -3.73 P-Value = 0.002
```

The output indicates that the mean for the Pretest is 97.06 and for the Posttest it is 107.83. The difference between the pretest and posttest is -10.77. If the p-value is less than your significance level, the difference does not equal zero.

Because our p-value (0.002) is less than the standard significance level of 0.05, we can reject the null hypothesis. Our sample data support the hypothesis that the population means are different. Specifically, the Posttest mean is greater than the Pretest mean.

Again, the sample estimate of the difference (-10.77) is unlikely to equal the population difference. The confidence interval estimates that the actual population difference between the Pretest and Posttest is likely between -16.96 and -4.59.

The negative values reflect the fact that the Pretest has a lower mean than the Posttest (i.e., Pretest – Posttest < 0). The confidence interval excludes the value of zero (no difference between groups), so we can conclude that the population rates are different.

If high scores are better, then the Posttest scores are significantly better than the pretest scores.

Paired t-Tests Are Really 1-Sample t-Tests

I've seen a lot of confusion over how a paired t-test works and when you should use it. Pssst! Here's a secret! Paired t-tests and 1-sample t-tests are the same hypothesis test incognito!

You use a 1-sample t-test to assess the difference between a sample mean and the null hypothesis value.

A paired t-test takes paired observations (like before and after), subtracts one from the other, and conducts a 1-sample t-test on the differences. Typically, a paired t-test determines whether the paired differences are significantly different from zero.

Analyze the CSV data file to check this yourself: T-testData. All of the statistical results are the same when you perform a paired t-test using the Before and After columns versus performing a 1-sample t-test on the Differences column.

Before	After	Difference
-1.432329	1.00369	-2.4360188
-1.439525	1.625069	-3.0645934
-0.878131	-0.07925	-0.7988785
2.046179	0.479616	1.5665631
-0.062343	1.205168	-1.2675111
0.837849	1.337103	-0.4992547
0.604821	2.555018	-1.9501968
1.648016	1.221696	0.4263201
0.250996	-0.22138	0.4723725
-0.399081	1.464167	-1.8632473
-1.945189	1.726297	-3.6714868
0.157812	0.72569	-0.5678778
-1.594282	0.313246	-1.9075278
0.478715	1.573126	-1.094411
1.764385	0.034644	1.7297405

Paired T-Test and CI: Before, After

```
Paired T for Before - After

              N    Mean   StDev   SE Mean
Before       15   0.003   1.276    0.329
After        15   0.998   0.779    0.201
Difference   15  -0.995   1.575    0.407

95% CI for mean difference: (-1.867, -0.123)
T-Test of mean difference = 0 (vs ≠ 0):
T-value = -2.45 P-Value = 0.028
```

One-Sample T: Score

Test of μ = 60 vs $\neq$ 60

Variable	N	Mean	StDev	SE Mean	95% CI	T	P
Fuel Cost	15	64.16	11.35	2.93	(57.87, 70.45)	1.42	0.178

When you realize that paired t-tests are the same as 1-sample t-tests on paired differences, you can focus on the deciding characteristic — does it make sense to analyze the differences between two columns?

Suppose the Before and After columns contain test scores and there was an intervention in between. If each row in the dataset contains the same subject in the two columns, it makes sense to find the difference between the columns. It represents how much each subject changed after the intervention. The paired t-test is the correct choice.

On the other hand, if a row has different subjects in the two columns, it doesn't make sense to subtract the columns. You should use the 2-sample t-test.

The paired t-test is a convenience for you. It eliminates the need for you to calculate the difference between two columns yourself. Remember, double-check that this difference is meaningful!

Why Not Accept the Null Hypothesis?

In the one-sample t-test example earlier in this chapter, our p-value was greater than the significance level. Consequently, we failed to reject the null hypothesis.

Failing to reject the null hypothesis is an odd way to state that the results of your hypothesis test are not statistically significant. Why the peculiar phrasing? "Fail to reject" sounds like one of those double negatives that writing classes taught you to avoid. What does it mean exactly? There's an excellent reason for the odd wording!

In this section, learn what it means when you fail to reject the null hypothesis and why that's the correct wording. While accepting the null hypothesis sounds more straightforward, it is not statistically accurate!

Before proceeding, let's recap some necessary information. In all hypothesis tests, you have the following two hypotheses:

- The null hypothesis states that there is no effect or relationship between the variables.
- The alternative hypothesis states the effect or relationship exists.

We assume that the null hypothesis is correct until we have enough evidence to suggest otherwise.

After you perform a hypothesis test, there are only two possible outcomes.

- When your p-value is less than or equal to your significance level, you reject the null hypothesis. The data favors the alternative hypothesis. Congratulations! Your results are statistically significant.
- When your p-value is greater than your significance level, you fail to reject the null hypothesis. Your results are not significant. That's the topic for this section.

To understand why we don't accept the null, consider that you can't prove a negative. A lack of evidence isn't proof that something doesn't exist. You just haven't proven that it exists. It might exist, but your study missed it. That's a huge difference, and it is the reason for the convoluted wording. Let's look at several analogies.

Species Presumed to be Extinct

Australian Tree Lobsters were assumed to be extinct. There was no evidence that any were still living because no one had seen them for decades. Yet in 1960, scientists observed them. The same thing happened to the Gracilidris Ant and the Nelson Shrew, among many others. Dedicated scientists were looking for these species but hadn't been in the right time and place to observe them. Lack of proof doesn't represent proof that something doesn't exist!

Criminal Trials

In a trial, we start with the assumption that the defendant is innocent until proven guilty. The prosecutor must work hard to exceed an evidentiary standard to obtain a guilty verdict. If the prosecutor does not meet that burden, it doesn't prove the defendant is innocent. Instead, there was insufficient evidence to conclude he is guilty.

Perhaps the prosecutor conducted a shoddy investigation and missed clues? Or, the defendant successfully covered his tracks? Consequently, the verdict in these cases is "not guilty." That judgment doesn't say the defendant is proven innocent, just that there wasn't enough evidence to move the jury from the default assumption of innocence.

Hypothesis Tests

When you're performing hypothesis tests in statistical studies, you typically want to find an effect or relationship between variables. The default position in a hypothesis test is that the null hypothesis is correct. Like a court case, the sample evidence must exceed the evidentiary standard, which is the significance level, to conclude that an effect exists.

The hypothesis test assesses the evidence in your sample. If your test fails to detect an effect, that's not proof it doesn't exist. It just means your sample contained an insufficient amount of evidence to conclude that it exists. Like the "extinct" species, or the prosecutor who missed clues, the effect might exist in the overall population but not in your particular sample. Consequently, the test results fail to reject the null hypothesis, which is analogous to a "not guilty" verdict in a trial. There just wasn't enough evidence to move the hypothesis test from the default position that the null is true.

The critical point across these analogies is that a lack of evidence does not prove something does not exist—just that you didn't find it in your specific investigation. Hence, you never accept the null hypothesis.

Interpreting Failures to Reject the Null

Accepting the null hypothesis would indicate that you've proven an effect doesn't exist. As you've seen, that's not the case at all. You can't prove a negative! Instead, the strength of your evidence falls short of being able to reject the null. Consequently, we fail to reject it.

Failing to reject the null indicates that our sample did not provide sufficient evidence to conclude that the effect exists. However, at the same time, that lack of evidence doesn't prove that the effect does not exist. Capturing all that information leads to the convoluted wording! What are the possible interpretations of failing to reject the null hypothesis? Let's work through them.

First, it is possible that the effect indeed doesn't exist in the population, so your hypothesis test didn't detect it in the sample. Makes sense, right? While that *is* one possibility, it doesn't end there.

Another possibility is that the effect exists in the population, but the test didn't detect it for a variety of reasons. These reasons include the following:

- The sample size was too small to detect the effect.
- The variability in the data was too high. The effect exists, but the noise (variability) in your data swamped the signal (effect).

52

- By chance, you collected a fluky sample. When dealing with random samples, chance always plays a role in the results. The luck of the draw might have caused your sample not to reflect an effect that exists in the population.

Notice in the first two bullets how studies that collect a small amount of data or low-quality data are likely to miss an effect that exists? These studies had an inadequate ability to detect the effect. We certainly don't want to take results from low-quality studies as proof that something doesn't exist!

However, failing to detect an effect does not necessarily mean a study is low-quality. Random chance in the sampling process can work against even the best research projects!

Using Confidence Intervals to Compare Means

We're shifting gears to close this chapter. The previous sections showed you different ways to compare means using t-tests. This section shows you one way NOT to compare two means that I've seen people use too often.

Analysts often compare the confidence intervals for two groups to determine whether the difference between two means is statistically significant. If those intervals overlap, they conclude that the difference between groups is not statistically significant. If there is no overlap, the difference is significant.

While this visual method of assessing the overlap is easy to perform, it regrettably reduces your ability to detect differences. Fortunately, there is a simple solution to this problem that allows you to perform a simple visual assessment and yet not diminish the power of your analysis.

I'll start by showing you the problem in action and explain why it happens. Then, we'll proceed to an easy alternative method that avoids this problem.

Determining whether confidence intervals overlap is an overly conservative approach for identifying significant differences between groups. It's true that when confidence intervals don't overlap, the difference between groups is statistically significant. However, when there is some overlap, the difference might still be significant.

Suppose you're comparing the mean strength of products from two groups and graph the 95% confidence intervals for the group means, as shown below. Following along with the CSV dataset that I use throughout this section: DifferenceMeans.

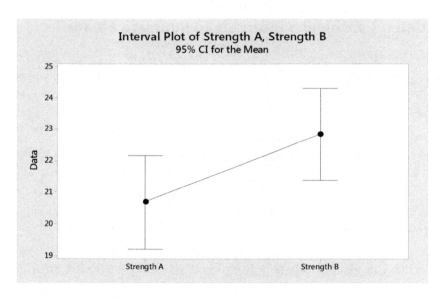

Jumping to Conclusions

Upon seeing how these intervals overlap, you conclude that the difference between the group means is not statistically significant. After all, if they're overlapping, they're not different, right?

This conclusion sounds logical, but it's not necessarily true. In fact, for these data, the 2-sample t-test results are statistically significant with a p-value of 0.044. Despite the overlapping confidence intervals, the difference between these two means is statistically significant.

This example shows how the CI overlapping method fails to reject the null hypothesis more frequently than the corresponding hypothesis test. Using this method decreases your ability to detect differences, potentially causing you to miss essential findings.

This apparent discrepancy between confidence intervals and hypothesis test results might surprise you. Analysts expect that confidence intervals with a confidence level of $(100 - X)$ will always agree with a hypothesis test that uses a significance level of X percent. For example, analysts often pair 95% confidence intervals with tests that use a 5% significance level. It's true. Confidence intervals and hypothesis tests should always agree. So, what is happening in the example?

Using the Wrong CIs

The problem occurs because we are not comparing the correct confidence intervals to the hypothesis test result. The test results apply to the difference between the means while the CIs apply to the estimate of each group's mean—not the difference between the means. We're comparing apples to oranges, so it's not surprising that the results differ.

To obtain consistent results, we must use confidence intervals for differences between group means—we'll get to those CIs shortly.

However, if you doggedly want to use CIs of each group to make this determination, there are several possible methods.

Goldstein and Healy find that for barely non-overlapping intervals to represent a 95% significant difference between two means, use an 83% confidence interval of the mean for each group. The graph below uses this confidence level for the previous dataset, and they don't overlap. (Goldstein & Healy, 1995)

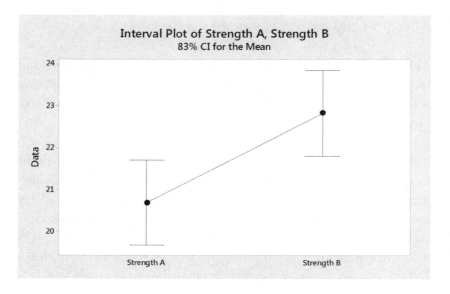

Cumming and Finch find that the degree of overlap for two 95% confidence intervals for independent means allows you to estimate the p-value for a 2-sample t-test when sample sizes are greater than 10. When the confidence limit of each CI reaches approximately the mid-point between the point estimate and the limit of the other CI, the p-value is near 0.05. (Cumming & Finch, 2005)

The first graph in this section, with the 95% CIs, approximates this condition, and the p-value is near 0.05. Lower amounts of overlap correspond to lower p-values. For 95% CIs, when the end of one CI just reaches the end of the other CI, it corresponds to a p-value of about 0.01.

To me, these approaches seem kludgy. Using a confidence interval of the difference is a more straightforward solution that even provides additional useful information.

Confidence Intervals of Differences

Previously, we saw how the apparent disagreement between the group CIs and the 2-sample test results occurs because we used the wrong confidence intervals. Instead, we need a CI for the difference between group means. This type of CI will always agree with the 2-sample t-test—just be sure to use the equivalent combination of confidence level and significance level (e.g., 95% and 5%). We're now comparing apples to apples!

Using the same dataset, the confidence interval below presents a range of values that likely contains the mean difference for the entire population. The interpretation continues to be a simple visual assessment. Zero represents no difference between the means. Does the interval contain zero? If it does not include zero, the difference is statistically significant because the range excludes no difference. At a glance, we can tell that the difference is statistically significant.

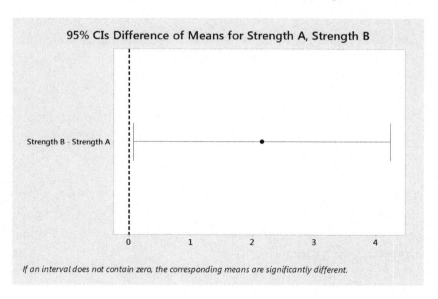

If an interval does not contain zero, the corresponding means are significantly different.

This graph corresponds with the following 2-sample t-test results. Both test the difference between the two means. This output also provides a numerical representation of the CI of the difference [0.06, 4.23].

```
┌─────────────────────────────────────────────────────────────┐
│ Two-Sample T-Test and CI: Strength B, Strength A              │
│                                                               │
│ Two-sample T for Strength B vs Strength A                     │
│                                                               │
│               N   Mean   StDev   SE Mean                      │
│ Strength B   20  22.84    3.08      0.69                      │
│ Strength A   20  20.69    3.41      0.76                      │
│                                                               │
│                                                               │
│ Difference = μ (Strength B) - μ (Strength A)                  │
│ Estimate for difference:   2.15                               │
│ 95% CI for difference:  (0.06, 4.23)                          │
│ T-Test of difference = 0 (vs ≠):                              │
│ T-Value = 2.09  P-Value = 0.044  DF = 37                      │
└─────────────────────────────────────────────────────────────┘
```

In addition to providing a simple visual assessment, the confidence interval of the difference presents crucial information that neither the group CIs nor the p-value provides. It answers the question, based on our sample, how large is the difference between the two populations likely to be? Like any estimate, there is a margin of error around the point estimate of the difference. It's important to factor in this margin of error before acting on findings.

For our example, the point estimate of the mean difference is 2.15, and we can be 95% confident that the population difference falls within the range of 0.06 to 4.23.

As with all CIs, the width of the interval for the mean difference reveals the precision of the estimate. Narrower intervals suggest a more precise estimate. And, you can assess whether the full range of values is practically significant.

When the interval is too wide (imprecise) to be helpful and/or the range includes differences that are not practically significant, you have reason to hesitate before making decisions based on the results.

These types of CI results indicate that you might not obtain meaningful benefits even though the difference is statistically significant.

There's no statistical method for answering questions about how precise an estimate must be or how large an effect must be to be practically useful. You'll need to apply your subject-area knowledge to the confidence interval of the difference to answer these questions.

For the example in this section, it's important to note that the low end of the CI is very close to zero. It would not be surprising if the actual population difference falls close to zero, which might not be practically significant despite the statistically significant result. If you are considering switching to Group B for a stronger product, the mean improvement might be too small to be meaningful.

When you're comparing groups, assess confidence intervals of those differences rather than comparing confidence intervals for each group. This method is simple, and it even provides you with additional valuable information.

Review and Next Steps

You're already interpreting test results from three different types of t-tests! Not too bad!

We also looked at the assumptions you need to consider for all these tests. If your data collection methodology and the properties of your data don't satisfy these assumptions, you might not be able to trust your results. However, it's important to remember that some assumptions are strong requirements (i.e., representative sample), while you can waive others when your sample is large enough (i.e., normality assumption).

In this chapter, we mainly looked at the sample means, p-values, and confidence intervals. However, I'm sure you noticed there are other values in the output. While we looked at the most important statistics for determining statistical significance, the other statistics represent crucial aspects of how the tests work. The upcoming chapters will systematically explain these additional statistics.

You learned that we do not accept the null hypothesis. Instead, we fail to reject it. The convoluted wording encapsulates the fact that insufficient evidence for an effect in our sample isn't proof that the effect does not exist in the population. The effect might exist, but our sample didn't detect it—just like all those species scientists presumed were extinct because they didn't see them.

Finally, I admonished you not to use the common practice of seeing whether confidence intervals of the mean for two groups overlap to determine whether the means are different. That process can cause you to overlook significant results and miss out on important information about the likely range of the mean difference. Instead, assess the confidence interval of the difference between means.

One of the statistics in the output for t-tests is the t-value, which is a test statistic. T-tests are named after the t-values and t-distributions they use to determine statistical significance. In chapter 3, you learn about test statistics, sample sizes, data variability, and how they all relate to sampling distributions and the outcome of the hypothesis test.

Test Statistics and Their Sampling Distributions

In this chapter, I'll introduce you to several components of hypothesis tests that are working behind the scenes, test statistics and their sampling distributions. Parametric hypothesis tests use them to determine statistical significance. Statisticians named many tests after their test statistics, such as t-tests, F-tests, and chi-squared tests. Each type of test is valid for particular kinds of data and for testing specific properties.

Chapter 1 discussed sampling distributions of the sample means and showed how you can place a sample mean into a sampling distribution of the means. However, hypothesis tests actually use test statistics and their sampling distributions for this purpose. I'll show you how that works in this chapter.

A test statistic is a value that hypothesis tests calculate from your sample data. These tests boil your data down into a single number, which measures the overall difference between your sample data and the null hypothesis.

Each test statistic has a sampling distribution that represents the test statistic's distribution if the null hypothesis is correct. By placing the test statistic for your data into the sampling distribution, the procedure can calculate how unusual your data are when you assume the null hypothesis is true.

For now, we'll continue to focus on t-tests. Later chapters will show how other types of tests use their test statistics and sampling distributions.

T-tests assess one or two sample means. When you analyze your data with any t-test, the procedure reduces your entire sample to a single value, the t-value. I'll describe how each type of t-test calculates the t-value. Understanding how these facets work will help you grasp the fundamentals of how t-tests work.

```
Difference = μ (1) - μ (2)
Estimate for difference:   -0.235
95% CI for difference:   (-1.450, 0.980)
T-Test of difference = 0  (vs ≠): T-Value = -0.38  P-Value = 0.701
```

As usual, I'll focus on ideas rather than formulas. However, I need to present a few easy equations to facilitate the analogy between how t-tests work and a signal-to-noise ratio.

A crucial point to remember throughout this chapter is that t-values measure the difference between your sample data and the null hypothesis. If your sample data exactly match the null hypothesis, the t-value equals zero.

How 1-Sample t-Tests Calculate t-Values

1-sample t-tests compare your sample mean to a null hypothesis value. We used a 1-sample t-test in the energy cost example to compare the sample mean of 330.6 to the null hypothesis value of 260.

1-sample t-tests take all your sample data and reduce it down to a single t-value. The equation for t-values in 1-sample t-tests is below:

$$t = \frac{\overline{X} - \mu_0}{s / \sqrt{n}}$$

This equation is a ratio, and a common analogy is the signal-to-noise ratio. The numerator is the signal in your sample data, and the denominator is the noise. Let's see how t-tests work by comparing the signal to the noise! I'll walk you through this equation by looking at the numerator and then the denominator.

The Signal - The Size of the Sample Effect

In the signal-to-noise analogy, the numerator of the ratio is the signal. The effect that is present in the sample is the signal. It's a simple calculation. In a 1-sample t-test, the sample effect is the sample mean minus the value of the null hypothesis. That's the top part of the equation.

For example, if the sample mean is 20 and the null value is 5, the sample effect size is 15. We're calling this the signal because this sample estimate is our best estimate of the population effect.

The calculation for the signal portion of t-values is such that when the sample effect equals zero, the numerator equals zero, which in turn means the t-value itself equals zero. The estimated sample effect (signal) equals zero when there is no difference between the sample mean and the null hypothesis value. For example, if the sample mean is 5 and the null value is 5, the signal equals zero (5 − 5 = 0).

The size of the signal increases when the difference between the sample mean and null value increases. The difference can be either negative or positive, depending on whether the sample mean is greater than or less than the value associated with the null hypothesis.

A relatively large signal in the numerator produces t-values that are further away from zero.

Now, we have to factor in the noise that can drown out the signal.

The Noise - The Variability or Random Error in the Sample

The denominator of the ratio is the standard error of the mean, which measures the sample variation. The standard error of the mean represents how much random error is in the sample and how well the sample estimates the population mean.

As the value of this statistic increases, the sample mean provides a less precise estimate of the population mean. In other words, high levels of random error increase the probability that your sample mean is further away from the population mean.

In our analogy, random error represents noise. Why? When there is more random error, you are more likely to see considerable differences between the sample mean and the null hypothesis value in cases where *the null is true*. Noise appears in the denominator to provide a benchmark for how large the signal must be to distinguish from the noise.

Signal-to-Noise ratio

Our signal-to-noise ratio analogy equates to:

$$t = \frac{\text{Estimated effect size (signal)}}{\text{Standard error of the mean (noise)}}$$

Both of these statistics are in the same units as your data. Let's calculate a couple of t-values to see how to interpret them.

- If the signal is 10 and the noise is 2, your t-value is 5. The signal is 5 times the noise.
- If the signal is 10 and the noise is 5, your t-value is 2. The signal is 2 times the noise.

The signal is the same in both examples, but it is easier to distinguish from the lower amount of noise in the first example. In this manner, t-values indicate how clear the signal is from the noise. If the signal is of the same general magnitude as the noise, random error likely causes the difference between the sample mean and null value rather than an actual population difference.

Remember, hypothesis tests help you separate real population effects from random sampling error. The t-value ratio is how t-tests accomplish that.

How Two-Sample T-tests Calculate T-Values

Use the 2-sample t-test when you want to analyze the difference between the means of two independent samples. This procedure reduces all your data to a single t-value in a process similar to the 1-sample t-test. The signal-to-noise analogy still applies.

Here's the equation for the t-value in a 2-sample t-test.

$$t = \frac{\overline{X}_1 - \overline{X}_2}{s}$$

The equation is still a ratio, and the numerator still represents the signal. For a 2-sample t-test, the signal, or effect, is the difference between the two sample means. This calculation is straightforward. If the first sample mean is 20 and the second mean is 15, the effect is 5.

Typically, the null hypothesis states that there is no difference between the two samples. In the equation, if both groups have the same mean, the numerator, and the ratio as a whole, equals zero. Larger differences between the sample means produce stronger signals.

The denominator again represents the noise for a 2-sample t-test. However, you can use two different values depending on whether you assume that the variation in both groups are equal. Most statistical software let you choose which value to use.

Regardless of the denominator value you use, the 2-sample t-test works by determining how distinguishable the signal is from the noise. To ascertain that the difference between means is statistically significant, you need a high positive or negative t-value.

Here's what we've learned about the t-values for the 1-sample t-test, paired t-test, and 2-sample t-test:

- Each test reduces your sample data down to a single t-value based on the ratio of the effect size to the variability in your sample.
- A t-value of zero indicates that your sample results match the null hypothesis precisely.
- Larger absolute t-values represent stronger signals, or effects, that stand out more from the noise.

For example, a t-value of 2 indicates that the signal is twice the magnitude of the noise.

Great ... but how do you get from the t-value to determining whether the effect size is statistically significant? After all, the purpose of t-tests is to assess hypotheses.

t-Distributions and Statistical Significance

The term "t-test" refers to the fact that these hypothesis tests use t-values to evaluate your sample data. T-values are a test statistic that factors in the effect size, sample size, and variability. Hypothesis tests use the test statistic that is calculated from your sample to compare your sample to the null hypothesis. If the test statistic is extreme enough, this indicates that your data are so incompatible with the null hypothesis that you can reject the null.

Don't worry. I find these technical definitions of statistical terms are easier to explain with graphs, and we'll get to that!

The tricky thing about t-values is that they are difficult to interpret on their own. Imagine we performed a t-test, and it produced a t-value of 2. What does this t-value mean exactly?

We know that the sample mean doesn't equal the null hypothesis value because this t-value doesn't equal zero. We can also state that the effect is twice the variability. However, we don't know how exceptional our value is if the null hypothesis is correct.

To be able to interpret individual t-values, we must place them in a larger context. T-distributions provide this broader context so we can determine the unusualness of an individual t-value.

What Are t-Distributions?

A single t-test produces a single t-value. Now, imagine the following process. First, let's assume that the null hypothesis is true for the population. Now, suppose we repeat our study many times by drawing numerous random samples of the same size from this population. Next, we perform t-tests on all the samples and plot the distribution of the t-values. This distribution is known as a sampling distribution, which is a type of probability distribution.

If we follow this procedure, we produce a graph that displays the distribution of t-values that we obtain from a population where the null hypothesis is true. We use sampling distributions to calculate probabilities for how unusual our sample statistic is if the null hypothesis is true.

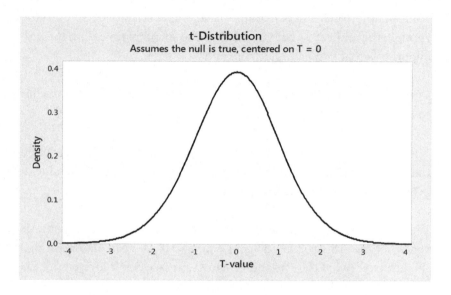

Luckily, we don't need to go through the hassle of collecting numerous random samples to create this graph! Statisticians understand the properties of t-distributions so we can estimate the sampling distribution using the t-distribution and our sample size.

The degrees of freedom (DF) for the statistical design define the t-distribution for a particular study. We'll go over degrees of freedom in more detail in a later chapter. For now, understand that degrees of freedom are closely related to the sample size. For t-tests, there is a different t-distribution for each sample size.

Use the t-Distribution to Compare Your Sample Results to the Null Hypothesis

T-distributions assume that the null hypothesis is correct for the population from which you draw your random samples. To evaluate how compatible your sample data are with the null hypothesis, place your study's t-value in the t-distribution and determine how unusual it is. Importantly, t-distributions are probability distributions, which means you can use them to calculate probabilities for regions of the distribution.

The sampling distribution below displays a t-distribution with 20 degrees of freedom, which equates to a sample size of 21 for a 1-sample t-test. The t-distribution centers on zero because it assumes that the null hypothesis is correct. When the null is true, your study is most likely to obtain a t-value near zero and less liable to produce t-values further from zero in either direction.

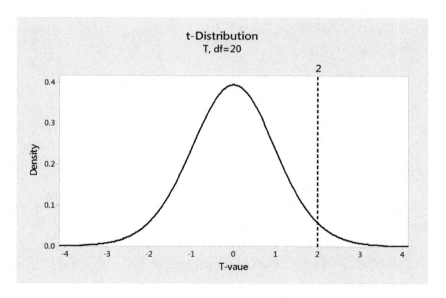

On the graph, I've displayed the t-value of 2 from our hypothetical study to see how our sample data compares to the null hypothesis. Under the assumption that the null is true, the t-distribution indicates that our t-value is not the most likely value. However, there still appears to be a realistic chance of observing t-values from -2 to +2.

We know that our t-value of 2 is rare when the null hypothesis is true. How rare is it exactly? Our final goal is to evaluate whether our sample t-value is so rare that it justifies rejecting the null hypothesis for the entire population based on our sample data. To proceed, we need to quantify the probability of observing our t-value.

Using t-Values and t-Distributions to Calculate Probabilities

Hypothesis tests work by taking the observed test statistic from a sample and using the sampling distribution to calculate the probability of obtaining that test statistic if the null hypothesis is correct. In the context of how t-tests work, you assess the likelihood of a t-value using the t-distribution. If a t-value is sufficiently improbable when the null hypothesis is true, you can reject the null hypothesis.

I have two crucial points to explain before we calculate the probability linked to our t-value of 2.

Because I'm showing the results of a two-tailed test, we'll use the t-values of +2 and -2. Two-tailed tests allow you to assess whether the sample mean is greater than or less than the target value in a 1-sample t-test. A one-tailed hypothesis test can only determine statistical significance for one or the other.

Additionally, it is possible to calculate a probability only for a range of t-values. On a probability distribution plot, probabilities are represented by the shaded area under a distribution curve. Without a range of values, there is no area under the curve and, hence, no probability.

Considering these points, the graph on the next page finds the probability associated with t-values less than -2 and greater than +2 using the area under the curve. This graph is specific to our t-test design (1-sample t-test with N = 21).

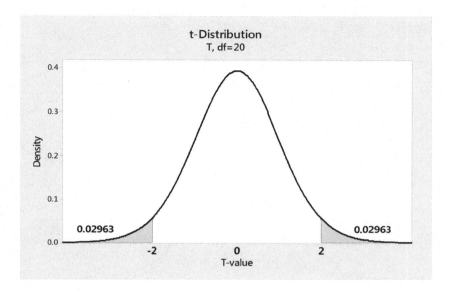

The probability distribution plot indicates that each of the two shaded regions has a probability of 0.02963—for a total of 0.05926. This graph shows that t-values fall within these areas almost 6% of the time when the null hypothesis is true.

There is a chance that you've heard of this type of probability before— it's the p-value! While the likelihood of t-values falling within these regions seems small, it's not quite unlikely enough to justify rejecting the null under the standard significance level of 0.05.

t-Distributions and Sample Size

The sample size for a t-test determines the degrees of freedom (DF) for that test, which specifies the t-distribution. The overall effect is that as the sample size decreases, the tails of the t-distribution become thicker. Thicker tails indicate that t-values are more likely to be far from zero even when the null hypothesis is correct. The changing shapes are how t-distributions factor in the greater uncertainty when you have a smaller sample.

You can see this effect in the probability distribution plot below that displays t-distributions for 5 and 30 DF.

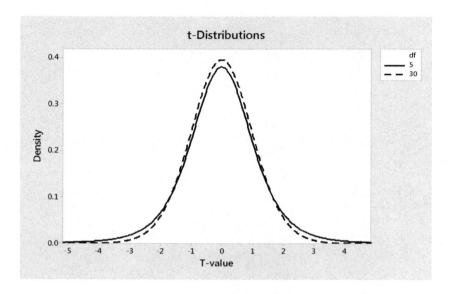

Sample means from smaller samples tend to be less precise. In other words, with a smaller sample, it's less surprising to have an extreme t-value, which affects the probabilities and p-values. A t-value of 2 has a p-value of 10.2% and 5.4% for 5 and 30 DF, respectively. Use larger samples!

Z-tests versus t-tests

Z-tests are very similar to t-tests. You use both kinds of tests for the same reasons—comparing means. Both types of tests have one-sample, two-sample, and paired versions. They even have the same assumptions—with one major exception. That difference determines when you'll use a Z-test versus t-test.

- **Z-test**: Use when you know the population standard deviation.
- **t-Test**: Use when you have an estimate of the population standard deviation.

I'm not covering Z-tests in this book for one excellent reason. You'll never use one in practice!

Think about it. The Z-test assumes that you know the population standard deviation. That rarely happens. In what situation would you not know the population mean (hence, the need to test it), but yet you do know the population standard deviation? As I discussed earlier, these parameters are generally unknowable.

Despite this critical limitation, many statistics students learn about Z-tests. Why is that? Many statistics textbooks use Z-tests because it is easier for students to calculate manually. However, the t-test is more accurate, particularly for smaller sample sizes. For more information about manually calculating Z-scores and using them to calculate probabilities, read my *Introduction to Statistics* book.

Z-tests use the standard normal distribution (mean = 0, standard deviation = 1) to calculate p-values while t-tests use the t-distribution. However, the t-distribution can approximate the normal distribution.

When statisticians say that a particular distribution approximates the normal distribution, it simply means that they have very similar shapes under certain conditions. T-distributions with at least 30 degrees of freedom will closely follow the normal distribution. Using either of the following two distributions to calculate p-values will produce similar results.

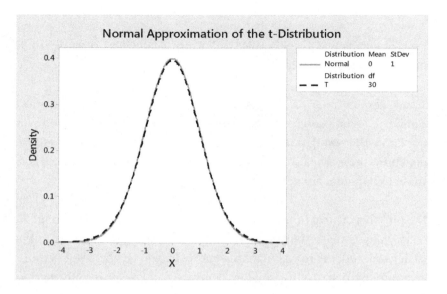

However, t-distributions with fewer degrees of freedom do not ap-proximate the normal distribution adequately. Consequently, using Z-tests with smaller samples will produce inaccurate results. In fact, William Sealy Gosset specifically developed the t-distribution to be able to analyze smaller samples.

As you will learn later in this book, probability distributions that other tests use can also approximate the normal distribution. Consequently, some tests produce multiple p-values, an exact test result and a normal approximation result.

Because I am assuming you'll use statistical software rather than per-forming manual calculations, I focus on the exact test results and ig-nore the normal approximations. Similarly, I don't cover Z-tests. However, if you ever find yourself needing to interpret Z-tests for means, use the same approach as we did for t-tests. Remember that Z-tests are inaccurate for smaller sample sizes (t df < 30) unless you gen-uinely know the population standard deviation.

Review and Next Steps

Hypothesis testing uses sampling distributions to calculate probabilities related to our data under the assumption that the null hypothesis is true. If the probability is low, our data are unlikely assuming the null is true. When the p-value is less than the significance level, our data is sufficiently incompatible with the null hypothesis that we can reject it. Our results are statistically significant, which indicates that our data favor the alternative hypothesis.

A critical aspect to remember is that t-distributions assume the null hypothesis is correct. In turn, p-values also follow that same assumption because they come from the t-distribution. Those principles apply to the distributions, and the resultant p-values, that other hypothesis tests use. Most people get tripped up and misinterpret p-values because they do not understand that p-values assume the null is true.

The next chapter focuses on interpreting p-values. I know what you're thinking. We already covered them. If the p-value is low, the null must go! And, you saw how they come from probability distributions.

However, that's just the outcome of the hypothesis test. There is an interpretation of the specific value itself. If you can keep the sampling distributions for the test statistic and its assumption of a true null hypothesis in mind, you'll have an advantage for understanding how to interpret p-values correctly!

CHAPTER 4

Interpreting P-values

Any time you see a p-value, you know you're looking at the results of a hypothesis test. P-values determine whether your hypothesis test results are statistically significant. If your p-value is less than the significance level, you can reject the null hypothesis and conclude that the effect or relationship exists. In other words, your sample evidence is strong enough to determine that the effect exists in the population.

Statistics use p-values all over the place. You'll find p-values in t-tests, distribution tests, ANOVA, and regression analysis. They have become so crucial that they've taken on a life of their own. They can determine which studies are published, which projects receive funding, and which university faculty members become tenured!

Ironically, despite being so influential, p-values are misinterpreted very frequently.

What *is* the correct interpretation of p-values? What do p-values *really* mean? That's the topic of this chapter!

P-values are a slippery concept. Don't worry. I'll explain p-values using an intuitive, concept-based approach so you can avoid making a widespread misinterpretation that can cause serious problems.

It's All About the Null Hypothesis

P-values are directly connected to the null hypothesis, as you hopefully remember from our discussion about sampling distributions for test statistics. So, we need to cover that first!

In all hypothesis tests, the researchers are testing an effect or relationship of some sort. The effect can be the effectiveness of a new vaccination, the durability of a new product, and so on. There is some benefit or difference that the researchers hope to identify.

However, it's possible that there actually is no effect or no difference between the experimental groups. In statistics, we call this lack of an effect the null hypothesis. When you assess the results of a hypothesis test, you can think of the null hypothesis as the devil's advocate position, or the position you take for the sake of argument.

To understand this idea, imagine a hypothetical study for medication that we know is entirely useless. In other words, the null hypothesis is true. There is no difference in patient outcomes at the population level between subjects who take the medication and subjects who don't.

Despite the null being accurate, you will likely observe an effect in the sample data due to random sampling error. It is improbable that samples will ever exactly equal the null hypothesis value.

Think back to those t-distributions centered on zero for no effect. With those distributions, we noticed that it is not unusual to have a sample effect even when the null hypothesis is correct. Therefore, the position hypothesis tests take for the sake of argument (devil's advocate) is that random sample error produces the observed sample effect rather than it being an actual effect.

Defining P-values

P-values indicate the believability of the devil's advocate case that the null hypothesis is correct given the sample data. They gauge how consistent your sample statistics are with the null hypothesis. Specifically, if the null hypothesis is right, what is the probability of obtaining an effect at least as large as the one in your sample?

- High p-values: Your sample results are consistent with a true null hypothesis.
- Low p-values: Your sample results are not consistent with a true null hypothesis.

If your p-value is small enough, you can conclude that your sample is so incompatible with the null hypothesis that you can reject the null for the entire population. P-values are an integral part of inferential statistics because they help you use your sample to draw conclusions about a population.

Here is the technical definition of p-values:

P-values are the probability of observing a sample statistic that is at least as extreme as your sample statistic when you assume that the null hypothesis is correct.

Let's go back to our hypothetical medication study. Suppose the hypothesis test generates a p-value of 0.03. You'd interpret this p-value as follows:

If the medicine has no effect in the population, 3% of studies will obtain the effect observed in your sample, or larger, because of random sample error.

Key Point: How probable are your sample data if the null hypothesis is correct? That's the only question that p-values answer.

This restriction segues to a persistent and problematic misinterpretation.

P-values Are *NOT* an Error Rate

Unfortunately, p-values are frequently misinterpreted. A common mistake is that they represent the likelihood of rejecting a null hypothesis that is actually true (Type I error). The idea that p-values are the probability of making a mistake is WRONG!

You can't use p-values to calculate the error rate directly for several reasons.

First, p-value calculations assume that the null hypothesis is correct. Thus, from the p-value's point of view, the null hypothesis is 100% true. Remember, p-values assume that the null is true, and sampling error caused the observed sample effect.

Second, p-values tell you how consistent your sample data are with a true null hypothesis. However, when your data are very inconsistent with the null hypothesis, p-values can't determine which of the following two possibilities is more probable:

- The null hypothesis is true, but your sample is unusual due to random sampling error.
- The null hypothesis is false.

To figure out which option is right, you must apply expert knowledge of the study area and, very importantly, assess the results of similar studies.

Going back to our medication study, let's highlight the correct and incorrect way to interpret the p-value of 0.03:

- **Correct:** Assuming the medication has zero effect in the population, you'd obtain the sample effect, or larger, in 3% of studies because of random sample error.
- **Incorrect:** There's a 3% chance of making a mistake by rejecting the null hypothesis.

Yes, I realize that the incorrect definition seems more straightforward, and that's why it is so common. Unfortunately, using this definition gives you a false sense of security, as I'll show you next.

What Is the True Error Rate?

The difference between the correct and incorrect interpretation is not just a matter of wording. There is a fundamental difference in the amount of evidence against the null hypothesis that each definition implies.

The p-value for our medication study is 0.03. If you interpret that p-value as a 3% chance of making a mistake by rejecting the null hypothesis, you'd feel like you're on pretty safe ground. However, after reading this section, you should realize that p-values are not an error rate, and you can't interpret them this way.

If the p-value is not the error rate for our study, what is the error rate? Hint: It's higher!

As I explained earlier, you can't directly calculate an error rate based on a p-value, at least not using the frequentist approach that produces p-values. However, you can estimate error rates associated with p-values by using Bayesian methodologies and simulation studies.

Sellke et al. have done this. While the exact error rate varies based on different assumptions, the values below use middle-of-the-road assumptions.

P-value	Probability of rejecting a true null hypothesis
0.05	At least 23% (and typically close to 50%)
0.01	At least 7% (and typically close to 15%)

These higher error rates probably surprise you! Regrettably, the common misconception that p-values are the error rate produces the false impression of considerably more evidence against the null hypothesis than is warranted. A single study with a p-value around 0.05 does not provide substantial evidence that the sample effect exists in the population.

These estimated error rates emphasize the need to have lower p-values and replicate studies that confirm the initial results before you can safely conclude that an effect exists at the population level. Additionally, studies with smaller p-values have higher reproducibility rates in follow-up studies.

In a nutshell, p-value calculations assume that the null hypothesis is correct and use that assumption to determine the likelihood of obtaining your observed sample data. P-values answer the question, "Are your sample data unusual if the null hypothesis is true?"

Here's a quick way to tell if you are misinterpreting p-values in hypothesis tests. If you interpret p-values as the probability that the null hypothesis is true or that rejecting the null hypothesis is a mistake, those are *incorrect* interpretations. Indeed, these are the most common misinterpretations of p-values that I addressed in the previous section.

Why Are P-values Misinterpreted So Frequently?

P-values are commonly misinterpreted. It's a very slippery concept that requires a lot of background knowledge to understand. Not surprisingly, I've received many questions about p-values in hypothesis testing over the years. However, one question stands out. *Why* are p-value misinterpretations so prevalent? I answer that question in this section and help you avoid making the same mistakes.

Historical Events Made P-values Confusing

The problem of misinterpreting p-values has existed for nearly a century. The origins go back to two rival camps in the early days of hypothesis testing. On one side, we have Ronald Fisher with his measures of evidence approach (p-values). And, on the other side, we have Jerzy Neyman and Egon Pearson with their error rate method (alpha). Fisher believed that you could use sample data to learn about a population. However, Neyman and Pearson thought that you couldn't learn from individual studies but only a long series of hypothesis tests.

Textbook publishers and statistics courses have squished together these two incompatible approaches. Today, the familiar hypothesis testing procedure of comparing p-values to alphas seems to fit together perfectly. However, they're based on irreconcilable methods.

I could say a lot about this forced merger. For the topic of this section, an important outcome is that p-values became associated with the Type I error rate, which is incorrect. A p-value is NOT an error rate, but alpha IS an error rate. By directly comparing the two values in a hypothesis test, it's easy to think they're both error rates. This misconception leads to the most common misinterpretations of p-values.

Fisher spent decades of his life trying to clarify the misunderstanding but to no avail.

P-values Don't Provide the Answers that We Really Want

Let's be honest. The common misinterpretations are what we really want to learn from hypothesis testing. We'd love to determine the probability that a hypothesis is correct. That *would* be nice. Unfortunately, hypothesis testing doesn't provide that kind of information. Instead, we obtain the likelihood of our *observation*. How likely is our sample if the null hypothesis is true? That's just not as helpful.

Think about this logically. Hypothesis tests use data from one sample exclusively. There is no outside reference to anything else in the world. You can't use a single sample to determine whether it represents the population. There's no basis for drawing conclusions like that.

Consequently, it's not possible to evaluate the probabilities associated with any hypotheses. To do that, we'd need a broader perspective than a single sample can provide. As an aside, Bayesian statistics attempt to construct this more comprehensive framework of probabilities.

P-values can't provide answers to what we really want to know. However, there is a persistent temptation to interpret them in this manner anyway. Remember, if you start to think of p-values as the probability of a hypothesis, you're barking up the wrong tree!

P-values Have a Torturous Definition

As I showed earlier, the correct definition of p-values is pretty convoluted. It is the probability of observing the data that you actually did observe in the hypothetical context that the null hypothesis is true. Huh? And, there is weird wording about being at least as extreme as your observation. It's just not intuitive. It takes a lot of studying to understand it all.

Unfortunately, the incorrect interpretations sound so much simpler than the correct interpretation. There is no straightforward *and* accurate definition of p-values that can compete against the simpler sounding misinterpretations. Indeed, not even scientists can explain p-values! And, so the errors continue.

Is Misinterpreting P-values Really a Problem?

Let's recap. Historical circumstances have linked p-values and the Type I error rate incorrectly. We have a natural inclination to want p-values to tell us more than they are able. There is no technically correct definition of the p-value that rolls off the tongue. There's nothing available to thwart the simpler and more tempting misinterpretation. It's no surprise that this problem persists! Even Fisher couldn't fix it!

As I explained in the previous section, the correct and incorrect interpretations are very different. If you believe that a p-value of 0.04 indicates that there is only a 4% chance that the null hypothesis is correct, you're in for a big surprise! It's often around 26%!

P-values and the Reproducibility of Experiments

At this point, I wouldn't blame you for wondering whether p-values are useful. They're confusing and they don't quite tell us what we most want to know. Let's do a reality check to see if p-values provide any real information!

Typically, when you perform a study, it's because you aren't sure whether the effect exists. After all, that's why you're performing the study, right? Consequently, when you get your results, whether they are statistically significant or not, you don't know conclusively whether the test results correctly match the underlying reality. We'd feel more confident in our statistical result if we knew that statistically significant results correspond to cases where the effect actually exists in the population.

So, how can we determine whether p-values are useful in the real world?

The ability to reproduce experimental results relate to p-values because both statistical concepts have similar foundations.

- P-values help you separate the signal of population level effects from the noise in sample data.
- Reproducible results support the notion that the findings can be generalized to the population rather than applying only to a specific sample.

So, p-values are related to reproducibility in theory. But, does this relationship exist in the real world? In this section, I present the findings of an exciting study that answers this question!

Let's cover the basics of replication and reproducibility quickly. Replication of a research study refers to repeating an experiment by using the same procedures but with a different sample. The researchers want to see if the replicate study reproduces the original findings.

Clearly, if the replicate study obtains similar findings, you can have more confidence in the results. When an effect exists in the population, it should be apparent in most random samples drawn from that population. Failure to reproduce the results raises the possibility that the original study was a fluke based on the sample's vagaries or some other problem.

The article we'll explore shines a beautiful empirical light on this matter. If lower p-values correspond to higher reproducibility rates, it suggests p-values provide meaningful information.

Estimating the Reproducibility Rate

Researchers for a study published in August 2015, *Estimating the reproducibility of psychological science*, wanted to estimate the reproducibility rate and to identify predictors for successfully reproducing experimental results in psychological studies. However, there was a shortage of replication studies available to analyze. Sadly, the lack exists because it is easier for authors to publish new results than to replicate prior studies. (Open Science Collaboration, 2015)

Because of this shortage, the group of 300 researchers first had to conduct their own replication studies. They identified 100 psychology studies with statistically significant findings that were published in three top psychology journals. Then, the research group replicated these 100 studies. After finishing the follow-up studies, they calculated the reproducibility rate and looked for predictors of success. To do this, they compared the results of each replicate study to the corresponding original study.

The researchers found that only 36 of the 100 replicate studies were statistically significant. That's a 36% reproducibility rate. This finding sent shock waves through the field of psychology!

My view of this low reproducibility rate is that science isn't a neat, linear process. It can be messy. For science, we take relatively small samples and attempt to model the complexities of the real world. When you're working with samples, false positives are an unavoidable part of the process.

Of course, it's going to take repeated experimentation to determine which results represent real findings rather than random noise in the data. You shouldn't expect a single study to prove anything conclusively. You need to do the replication studies.

P-values and Reproducibility Rates

The researchers evaluated various measures to see if they could predict the probability that a follow-up study will reproduce the original results. These potential predictors include the original researchers' professional traits, hypotheses, methodology, and strength of evidence measures, such as the p-value.

Most measures don't predict reproducibility rates. However, p-values are good predictors! The chart below shows how lower p-values in the original studies related to higher reproducibility rates in the replicate studies.

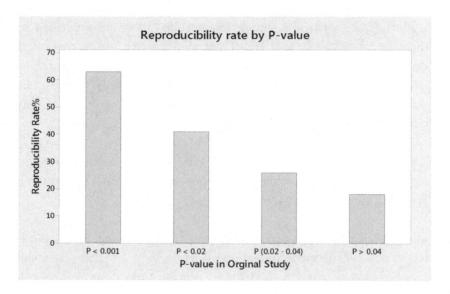

Obviously, p-values provide vital information about which studies are more likely to have reproducible results.

The reproducibility study reinforces highlights the following points:

- Knowing the precise p-value is essential—just reporting statistical significance is insufficient.
- A p-value near 0.05 isn't worth much by itself.
- Replication is crucial.

The low reproducibility rate reaffirms the critical role of replicating studies before determining that a finding has been experimentally established. I vehemently oppose the "one and done" practice that makes it easier to publish new studies than publishing replication studies. In my view, replication studies are just as critical as the original studies. After all, if it weren't for the 100 replication studies in this analysis, we'd have the wrong impression about 64% of the original experiments!

While p-values are confusing, they do provide valuable information about a study. You want very low p-values!

The Good Side of High P-values

Can high p-values be helpful? What do high p-values mean?

Typically, when you perform a hypothesis test, you want to obtain low p-values that are statistically significant. Small p-values are sexy. They represent exciting findings and can help you get articles published.

However, you might be surprised to learn that higher p-values, which are not statistically significant, are also valuable. Let's see the potential value of a p-value greater than 0.05, or whatever significance level you're using!

Hypothesis testing is a form of inferential statistics. You want to use your sample data to draw conclusions about the entire population. When you collect a random sample, you might observe an effect within the sample, such as a difference between group means. But, does that effect exist in the population? Or is it just random error in the sample?

For example, suppose you're comparing two teaching methods and determining whether one produces higher mean test scores. In your sample data, you see that the mean for Method A is greater than Method B. However, random samples contain random error, which makes your sample means very unlikely to equal the population means precisely. Unfortunately, the difference between the sample means of two teaching methods can represent either an effect in the population or random error in your sample.

This point is where p-values and significance levels come in. Typically, you want p-values that are less than your significance levels (e.g., 0.05) because it indicates your sample evidence is strong enough to conclude that Method A is better than Method B for the entire population. The teaching method appears to have a real effect. Exciting stuff!

However, I'll go in the opposite direction for now and try to help you appreciate higher, insignificant p-values! These are cases where you cannot conclude that an effect exists in the population. For the teaching method example, a higher p-value indicates that we have insufficient evidence to state that one teaching method is better than the other.

Let's graphically illustrate three different hypothetical studies about teaching methods in the following set of three plots. Which of these three studies have statistically significant results? The mean difference between the two groups is the effect size for each experiment. Use this CSV data file: studies.

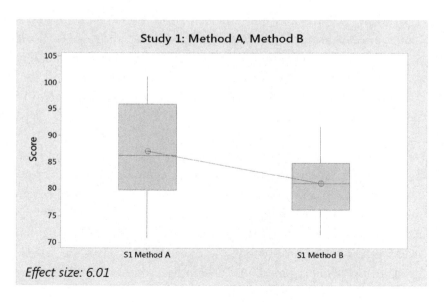

Effect size: 6.01

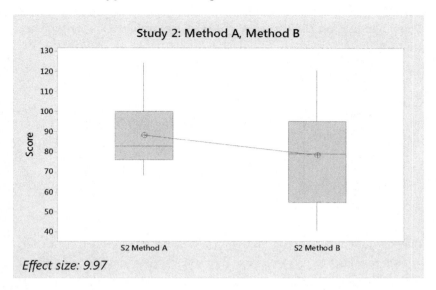

Effect size: 9.97

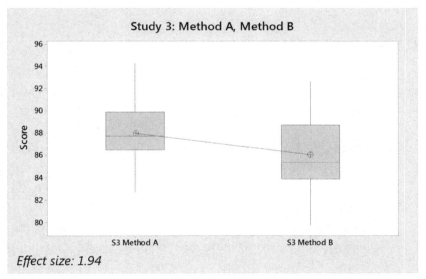

Effect size: 1.94

All three studies appear to have differences between their sample means. However, even if the population means are equal, the sample means are unlikely to be equal. We need to filter out the signal (real differences) from the noise (random error). That's where hypothesis tests play a role.

The table displays the p-values from the 2-sample t-tests for the three studies.

Study	Effect Size	P-value
1	6.01	0.116
2	9.97	0.140
3	1.94	0.042

Surprise! Only the graph with the smaller difference between means is statistically significant!

The key takeaway here is that you can use graphs to illustrate experimental results, but you must use hypothesis tests to draw conclusions about effects in the population. Don't jump to conclusions because the patterns in your graph might represent random error!

P-values Greater Than the Significance Level

A crucial point to remember is that the effect size that you see in the graphs is only one of several factors that influence statistical significance. These factors include the following:

- **Effect size**: Larger effect sizes are less likely to represent random error. However, by itself, the effect size is insufficient.
- **Sample size**: Larger sample sizes allow hypothesis tests to detect smaller effects.
- **Variability**: When your sample data are more variable, random sampling error is more likely to produce substantial differences between groups even when no effect exists in the population.

You can have a large effect size, but if your sample size is small and/or the variability in your sample is high, random error can produce substantial differences between the groups. High p-values help identify cases where random error is a likely culprit for differences between groups in your sample.

Studies one and two, which are not significant, show the protective function of high p-values in action. For these studies, the differences in the graphs might be random error even though it appears like there is a real difference. It's tempting to jump to conclusions and shout to the world that Method A is better, "Everyone, start teaching using Method A!"

However, the higher p-values for the first two studies indicate that our sample evidence is not strong enough to reject the notion that we're observing random sample error. If it is random error, Method A isn't actually producing better results than Method B. Instead, the luck of the draw created a sample where subjects in the Method A group were, by chance, able to score higher for some reason other than teaching method, such as a greater inherent ability.

If you perform the study again, it would not be surprising if the difference vanished or even went the other direction!

What High P-Values Mean and Don't Mean

As a reminder, high p-values don't prove there is no effect. High p-values indicate that your evidence is not strong enough to suggest an effect exists in the population. An effect might exist, but it's possible that the effect size is too small, the sample size is too small, or there is too much variability for the hypothesis test to detect it.

While you might not like obtaining results that are not statistically significant, these results can prevent you from jumping to conclusions and making decisions based on random noise in your data! High p-values help avoid costly mistakes. After all, if you base decisions on random error, you won't gain the benefits you expect. This protection applies to studies about teaching methods, medication effectiveness, product strength, and so on.

High p-values are a valuable caution against making rash decisions or drawing conclusions based on differences that look important but might be random error.

Practical vs. Statistical Significance

In the previous section, we looked at how a relatively large effect in your sample might really be random error. We saw how high p-values can protect you from jumping to conclusions based on the error. In this section, I help you avoid the opposite condition.

Imagine you've just performed a hypothesis test and your results are statistically significant. Hurray! These results are important, right? Not so fast. Statistical significance does not necessarily mean that the results are practically meaningful in the real world. You can have significant results for a small effect. Remember how the previous section showed how effect size was only one factor out of three?

In this section, I'll talk about the differences between practical significance and statistical significance, and how to determine if your results are meaningful in the real world.

Statistical Significance

The hypothesis testing procedure determines whether the sample results that you obtain are likely if you assume the null hypothesis is correct for the population. If the results are sufficiently improbable under that assumption, you can reject the null hypothesis and conclude that an effect exists. Your results are statistically significant.

Consequently, it might seem logical that p-values and statistical significance relate to importance. However, that is false because conditions other than large effect sizes can produce tiny p-values.

Hypothesis tests with small effect sizes can produce very low p-values when you have a large sample size and/or the data have low variability. Consequently, effect sizes that are trivial in the practical sense can be statistically significant.

Here's how small effect sizes can still produce tiny p-values:

You have a very large sample size. As the sample size increases, the hypothesis test gains greater ability to detect small effects. With a large enough sample size, the hypothesis test can detect an effect that is so miniscule that it is meaningless in a practical sense.

The sample variability is very low. When your sample data have low variability, hypothesis tests can produce more precise estimates of the population's effect. This precision allows the test to detect tiny effects.

Statistical significance indicates only that you have sufficient evidence to conclude that an effect exists. It is a mathematical definition that does not know anything about the subject area and what constitutes an important effect.

Practical Significance

Size matters!

While statistical significance relates to whether an effect exists, practical significance refers to its magnitude. However, no statistical test can tell you whether the effect is large enough to be important in your field of study. Instead, you need to apply your subject area knowledge and expertise to determine whether the effect is big enough to be meaningful in the real world. In other words, is it large enough to care about?

How do you do this? I find that it is helpful to identify the smallest effect size that still has some practical significance. Again, this process requires that you use your knowledge of the subject to make this determination. If your study's effect size is greater than this smallest meaningful effect, your results are practically significant.

For example, suppose you are evaluating a training program by comparing the test scores of program participants to those who study on their own. Further, we decide that the difference between these two groups must be at least five points to represent a practically meaningful effect size. An effect of 4 points or less is too small to be relevant.

After performing the study, the analysis finds a statistically significant difference between the two groups. Participants in the study program score an average of 3 points higher on a 100-point test. While these results are statistically significant, the 3-point difference is less than our 5-point threshold. Consequently, our study provides evidence that this effect exists, but it is too small to be meaningful in the real world. The time and money that participants spend on the training program are not worth an average improvement of only 3 points.

Not all statistically significant differences are interesting!

That sounds straightforward. Unfortunately, there is one small complication. Your effect size is only an estimate because it comes from a sample. Thanks to sampling error, there is a margin of error around it.

We need a method to determine whether the estimated effect is still practically significant when you factor in this margin of error. Enter confidence intervals!

A confidence interval is a range of values that likely contains the population value. I wrote about confidence intervals earlier, so I'll keep it short here. The central idea is that confidence intervals incorporate the margin of error by creating a range around the estimated effect. The population value is likely to fall within that range. Your task is to determine whether all, some, or none of that range represents practically significant effects.

Example of Using Confidence Intervals for Practical Significance

Suppose we conduct two studies on the training program described in the previous section. Both studies are statistically significant and produce an estimated effect of 9. These effects look good because they're both greater than our smallest meaningful effect size of 5. However, these estimates don't incorporate the margin of error. The confidence intervals (CIs) for both studies below provide that crucial information.

Study A CI	Study B CI
[3 15]	[7 11]

Study A's CI extends from values that are too small to be meaningful (<5) to those that are large enough to be meaningful. Even though the study is statistically significant and the estimated effect is 9, the CI creates doubt about whether the actual population effect is large enough to be important. The CI tells us that if we implement the program on a larger scale, we might produce only an average 3-point increase! We can't be sure about practical significance after we include the margin of error around the estimate.

On the other hand, the CI for Study B contains only meaningful effect sizes. We can be more confident that the population effect size is large enough for us to care!

As I wrote earlier, I really like confidence intervals because you can use them to determine both statistical significance (if they exclude zero) and practical importance. Confidence intervals focus on the size of the effect and the uncertainty around the estimate rather than just whether the effect exists.

In closing, statistical significance indicates that your sample provides enough evidence to conclude that the effect exists in the population. Practical significance asks whether that effect is substantial enough to be meaningful. Use p-values to determine statistical significance and subject-area expertise and confidence intervals to assess practical significance.

Practical Tips to Avoid Being Fooled

After reading the chapter to this point, you should have no doubts that understanding your hypothesis test result is not as simple as only whether your p-value is less than your significance level. Now, I'll build on the information we covered throughout this chapter and present practical advice that helps you assess and minimize the possibility of being fooled by false positives and other misleading results.

Previously, I showed how a common misconception about interpreting p-values produces the illusion of substantially more evidence against the null hypothesis than is justified. For example, a p-value near 0.05 often has a false positive error rate of between 23-50%. These greater than expected false positive rates create doubts about trusting statistically significant results. Relatedly, we saw how the reproducibility rate for psychology studies is surprisingly low.

When a hypothesis test produces significant results, there is always that chance that it is a false positive. In this context, a false positive occurs when you obtain a statistically significant p-value, and you unknowingly reject a null hypothesis that is actually true. You conclude that an effect exists in the population when it does not exist.

From a scientific point of view, the high false-positive rates are problematic because of the misleading results. From a practical standpoint, if you are using a hypothesis test to improve a product or process, you won't obtain the benefits that you expect if the test results are a false positive. That can cost you a lot of money!

Let's delve into the tips. These tips will help you develop a deeper understanding of your test results. I'll use a real AIDS vaccine study conducted in Thailand to work through these considerations. The study obtained a p-value of 0.039, which sounds great. Hurray, the vaccine works! However, after reading this book, you might think differently.

Tip 1: Smaller P-values are Better

Analysts often view statistical results as being either significant or not. The focus is on whether the p-value is less than the significance level because statistically significant results are highly prized. Unfortunately, that binary decision process is an oversimplification because no particular significance level correctly determines which studies have real population effects 100% of the time. Instead, we need to focus on understanding the relationship between false-positive rates and p-values.

Simulation studies find that lower false positive rates are associated with smaller p-values. For example, a p-value close to 0.05 usually has an error rate of 25-50%. However, a p-value of 0.0027 often has an error rate of around 4.5%. That error rate is close to the rate that is often erroneously ascribed to a p-value of 0.05.

Lower p-values indicate stronger evidence against the null hypothesis and a lower probability of a false positive. You can't hang your hat on a single study that produces a p-value near 0.05. Your p-value needs to be close to 0.002 before you can start to get excited over the statistical results from a single study.

It's important to note that there is no directly calculable relationship between p-values and the false positive rate. However, simulation studies and the Bayesian approach can produce ballpark estimates of the false positive rate. On the empirical side of things, studies with lower p-values have higher reproducibility rates in follow-up studies.

To help avoid misleading results, you should consider the exact value of the p-value. Using the binary approach of a yes or no determination of statistical significance is too simplistic.

The AIDS vaccine study has a p-value of 0.039. Based on the false positive rates, we should be cautious about this result.

Tip 2: Replication is Crucial

In the previous tip, I referred to results from a single study. Realistically, you need to replicate statistically significant results several times before you can have confidence in the conclusions.

In the high-pressure environment to obtain significant p-values, a single p-value is often considered conclusive. However, Ronald Fisher developed p-values with the notion that they are just one part of the scientific process that includes experimentation, analysis, and *replication.*

"A scientific fact should be regarded as experimentally established only if a properly designed experiment rarely fails to give this level of significance." –Ronald Fisher

The false-positive rates associated with a single study with a p-value between 0.01 and 0.05 are likely to be too high to be acceptable. In these cases, you need repeated experimentation with consistently significant results to be confident that the alternative hypothesis is correct.

Along these lines, you can think of p-values as probabilities that you can multiply. For example, if two independent studies have p-values of 0.05, you can multiply them to obtain a probability of 0.0025. If you use this approach, you can't cherry-pick the best studies. You must include all studies in a series of relevant studies, whether they are significant or not.

You should consider results from a study in conjunction with other similar studies. It is doubtful that a single study can prove that the alternative hypothesis is true with any confidence. So, don't expect that outcome!

For the AIDS vaccine study, the Thai experiment is the first AIDS vaccination study to produce statistically significant results. Other researchers have not replicated it, so we need to be wary of misleading results. This vaccine has not built up a track record of significant results.

Tip 3: The Effect Size is Important

The high pressure to obtain statistically significant p-values draws attention away from both the effect size and the estimate's precision. You can have statistically significant test results even when effect sizes are too small to be practically meaningful. Additionally, a significant p-value does not necessarily indicate that the analysis could estimate the effect size with high precision.

To place a greater emphasis on effect size and precision, use confidence intervals.

You should not think about statistical significance strictly from a binary perspective. Instead, consider whether the effect size is large enough to be practically important and if the estimate is sufficiently precise.

Unfortunately, the confidence interval for the effectiveness of the AIDS vaccine extends from 1% to 52%. The vaccine might work almost none of the time up to half the time. The confidence interval reveals that the estimated effect size is both small and imprecise. In this case, the p-value provides a misleading idea about what the data show.

Tip 4: The Plausibility of the Alternative Hypothesis Matters

As we evaluate p-values in hypothesis tests, there is a tendency to think that similar p-values across studies give comparable support for the alternative hypothesis. For example, a p-value of 0.04 in one study seems to provide the same evidence as a p-value of 0.04 in another study. However, simulation studies show that the plausibility of the study's alternative hypothesis considerably affects the false positive rate.

For instance, with a p-value of 0.05, a highly plausible alternative hypothesis is associated with a false positive rate of at least 12%. In comparison, an implausible alternative has a rate of at least 76%! If you are studying an unlikely alternative hypothesis and you obtain a significant p-value, there is a higher probability that the alternative hypothesis is not correct.

Extraordinary claims require extraordinary evidence—consider the plausibility of the alternative hypothesis in conjunction with the p-value. A significant p-value doesn't absolve us of using our common sense while interpreting the results. If you hear about a startling study that produces unprecedented results, don't let that initial significant p-value sway you too much. Wait until the other studies replicate the findings before you trust them!

No studies of other AIDS vaccines have provided sufficient evidence to reject the null hypothesis. This pattern demonstrates it is unlikely that the alternative hypothesis is correct for the Thai study. In this scenario, we can expect false-positive rates of around 75%! For this scenario, replicating the results with other studies is crucial—see tip #2.

Tip 5: Use Your Expertise

You must apply your subject area knowledge to all facets of hypothesis testing to avoid misleading results. Investigators should use their expertise to evaluate the validity of the experimental design, proposed mechanisms behind the effect, practical significance of the effect, the plausibility of the alternative hypothesis, and so on. Expertise transforms statistical results from numbers into meaningful findings that you can trust.

Evaluating the Hypothesis Test Results for the AIDS Vaccine Study

In this section, we looked at an AIDS vaccine study that had statistically significant results. However, we saw the following:

- The p-value of 0.039 is not compelling evidence by itself.
- The vaccine does not have a proven track record of significant results.
- The confidence interval indicates that the estimated effect size is both small and imprecise.
- Studies of other AIDS vaccines have not had significant results, suggesting that the alternative hypothesis in the Thai study is implausible.

Taking all of these points together, the additional considerations should make us cautious about potentially misleading results. In other words, we shouldn't pop open a bottle of champagne and start mass-producing the vaccine yet. We need to wait and see if other studies will replicate these results. We also need to keep an eye on the effect size in future studies to determine whether the vaccine's effectiveness is practically significant.

Now that's a much more thorough assessment than merely noting that the p-value is statistically significant!

Review and Next Steps

P-values are a slippery concept. Unfortunately, the common mistake analysts make when interpreting them creates the illusion of more persuasive evidence against the null hypothesis than what exists.

A variety of historical and practical considerations have conspired to keep this illusion alive. We really want to know the probability that a hypothesis is true or false. Unfortunately, p-values simply can't tell us that. Instead, they indicate the likelihood of obtaining the effect we observed in our dataset, or more extreme, if the null hypothesis is true.

So, p-values are confusing, don't tell us what we most want to know, and provide less evidence against the null than you might think. Despite these problems, p-values still provide valuable information. Both simulation studies and the empirical reproducibility study indicate that lower p-values are associated with real effects.

Additionally, there *are* essential considerations for the full range of p-values. P-values higher than your significance level can protect you from making decisions based on random error. Random error can create the appearance of an effect in your sample that doesn't exist in the population. Conversely, having a significant p-value doesn't necessarily indicate that the effect is large enough to be important in the real world. Check those confidence intervals!

Finally, we put all of this together into five tips for interpreting p-values for studies!

While hypothesis tests are great tools, they aren't perfect. The next chapter helps you understand the two types of errors in hypothesis testing.

CHAPTER 5

Types of Errors and Statistical Power

Hypothesis tests use sample data to make inferences about the properties of a population. As I've stated before, you gain tremendous benefits by working with random samples because it is usually impossible to measure the entire population.

However, there are tradeoffs when you use samples. The samples we use are typically a miniscule percentage of the entire population. Consequently, they occasionally misrepresent the population severely enough to cause hypothesis tests to make incorrect inferences.

In this chapter, you will learn about the two types of errors in hypothesis testing, their causes, and how to manage them. You'll also learn about statistical power and how to increase it. Power is the test's ability to detect an effect that actually exists. Increasing power is one way to manage testing errors.

Hypothesis testing is a procedure in inferential statistics that assesses two mutually exclusive theories about a population's properties. For a generic hypothesis test, the two hypotheses are as follows:

- **Null hypothesis**: There is no effect
- **Alternative hypothesis**: There is an effect.

The sample data must provide sufficient evidence to reject the null hypothesis and conclude that the effect exists in the population. Ideally, a hypothesis test fails to reject the null hypothesis when the effect is not present in the population, and it rejects the null hypothesis when the effect exists.

Statisticians define two types of errors in hypothesis testing. Creatively, they call these errors Type I and Type II errors. Both types of errors relate to incorrect conclusions about the null hypothesis.

The table summarizes the four possible outcomes for a hypothesis test.

	Test Rejects Null	**Test Fails to Reject Null**
Null is True	⊘ Type I error False positive	✓ Correct decision No effect
Null is False	✓ Correct decision Effect exists	⊘ Type II error False negative

Fire Alarm Analogy

A fire alarm provides a good analogy for the types of hypothesis testing errors. Ideally, the alarm rings when there is a fire and does not ring in the absence of a fire. However, if the alarm rings when there is no fire, it is a false positive, or a Type I error in statistical terms. Conversely, if the fire alarm fails to ring when there is a fire, it is a false negative, or a Type II error.

Using hypothesis tests correctly improves your chances of drawing trustworthy conclusions. However, errors are bound to occur.

Unlike the fire alarm analogy, there is no sure way to determine if an error occurred after performing a hypothesis test. You can look at the test results and evaluate whether they're statistically significant. But there are usually no warning signs when an error occurs. Typically, a clearer picture develops over time as other researchers conduct similar studies and an overall pattern of results appears. Seeing how your results fit in with similar studies is crucial in assessing your study's findings.

Let's look at each type of error in more depth.

Type I Errors: False Positives

When you see a p-value that is less than your significance level, you get excited because your results are statistically significant. However, it could be a type I error. The supposed effect might not exist in the population. Again, there are usually no warning signs when this occurs.

Why do these errors occur? It comes down to sample error. Your random sample has overestimated the effect by chance. It was the luck of the draw. This type of error doesn't indicate that the researchers did anything wrong. The experimental design, data collection, data validity, and statistical analysis can all be correct, yet this error still occurs.

Even though we don't know which studies have false-positive results, we *do* know their rate of occurrence. The rate of occurrence for Type I errors equals the significance level of the hypothesis test, also known as alpha (α).

The significance level is an evidentiary standard that you set to determine whether your sample data are strong enough to reject the null hypothesis. Hypothesis tests define that standard using the probability of rejecting a true null hypothesis. You set this value based on your willingness to risk a false positive.

If you think back to the sampling distributions, it makes sense. The sampling distributions assume the null hypothesis is correct. The significance level defines the critical regions. Therefore, when the null hypothesis is right, you expect test results to fall in the critical regions with a probability set by the significance level.

When the significance level is 0.05 and the null hypothesis is true, there is a 5% chance that the test will reject the null hypothesis incorrectly. If you set alpha to 0.01, there is a 1% of a false positive. If 5% is good, then 1% seems even better, right? As you'll see, there is a tradeoff between Type I and Type II errors. If you hold everything else constant, as you reduce the chance for a false positive, you increase the opportunity for a false negative.

Type I errors are relatively straightforward. Statisticians designed hypothesis tests to incorporate everything that affects this error rate, which allows you to specify it for your studies. If your experimental design is sound, you collect representative data, and the data satisfy the hypothesis test's assumptions, the Type I error rate equals the significance level that you specify. However, if there is a problem in one of those areas, it can affect the false positive rate.

Warning about a potential misinterpretation of Type I errors and the Significance Level

When the null hypothesis is correct for the population, the test's probability for a false positive equals the significance level. However, when you look at a statistically significant test result, you cannot state that there is a 5% chance that it represents a false positive.

Why is that the case? Imagine we perform 100 studies on a population where the null hypothesis is true. If we use a significance level of 0.05, we'd expect that five of the studies will produce statistically significant results—false positives. Afterward, when we look at those significant studies, what is the probability that each is a false positive? Not 5 percent but 100%!

That scenario also illustrates the point that I made earlier. An accurate picture becomes evident after repeated experimentation. Given the pattern of results that are predominantly not significant, it is unlikely that an effect exists in the population.

Type II Errors: False Negatives

When you perform a hypothesis test and your p-value is greater than your significance level, your results are not statistically significant. That's disappointing because your sample provides insufficient evidence for concluding that the effect you're studying exists in the population. However, there is a chance that the effect is present in the population even though the test results don't support it. If that's the case, you've just experienced a Type II error. The probability of making a Type II error is known as beta (β).

What causes Type II errors?

Let's revisit Type I errors briefly. When your study does everything correctly, sampling error is the one thing that causes Type I errors.

In comparison, there are multiple reasons for Type II errors—small effect sizes, small sample sizes, and high data variability. Furthermore, unlike Type I errors, you can't set the Type II error rate for your analysis. Instead, the best that you can do is estimate it before you begin your study by approximating properties of the alternative hypothesis that you're studying. When you do this type of estimation, it's called power analysis.

When estimating the Type II error rate, your statistical software creates a hypothetical probability distribution representing the properties of a true alternative hypothesis. However, when you're performing a hypothesis test, you typically don't know which hypothesis is true, much less the specific properties of the distribution for the alternative hypothesis. Consequently, the actual Type II error rate is usually unknown!

Type II Errors and Statistical Power

The Type II error rate (beta) is the probability of a false negative. Therefore, the inverse of Type II errors is the probability of correctly detecting an effect. Statisticians refer to this concept as the power of a hypothesis test. Consequently, $1 - \beta =$ the statistical power. Analysts typically estimate power rather than beta directly.

The three factors that affect power are sample size, variability in the population, and the effect size. As you design your experiment, you can enter estimates of these three factors into statistical software, and it calculates the estimated power for your test.

Suppose you perform a power analysis for an upcoming study and calculate an estimated power of 90%. For this study, the estimated Type II error rate is 10% $(1 - 0.9)$. Keep in mind that variability and effect size are estimates and guesses. Consequently, power and the Type II error rate are just estimates rather than something you set directly. These estimates are only as good as the inputs into your power analysis.

Low variability and larger effect sizes decrease the Type II error rate, which increases the statistical power. However, researchers usually have less control over those aspects of a hypothesis test. Typically, researchers have the most control over sample size, making it the critical way to manage your Type II error rate. Holding everything else constant, increasing the sample size reduces the Type II error rate and increases power.

Graphing Type I and Type II Errors

The graph illustrates the two types of errors using two sampling distributions. The critical value line represents the point at which you reject or fail to reject the null hypothesis. Of course, when you perform the hypothesis test, you don't know which hypothesis is correct. And, the properties of the distribution for the alternative hypothesis are usually unknown. However, use this graph to understand the general nature of these errors and how they are related.

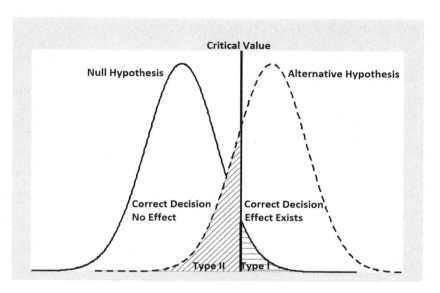

The distribution on the left represents the null hypothesis. When the null hypothesis is correct, you only need to worry about Type I errors, which is the shaded portion of the null hypothesis distribution. The rest of the null distribution shows the correct decision of failing to reject the null.

On the other hand, when the alternative hypothesis is right, you need to worry about Type II errors. The shaded region on the alternative hypothesis distribution represents the Type II error rate. The rest of the alternative distribution depicts the probability of correctly detecting an effect— which is statistical power.

Moving the critical value line is equivalent to changing the significance level. If you move the line to the left, you're increasing the significance level (e.g., α 0.05 to 0.10). Holding everything else constant, this adjustment increases the Type I error rate while reducing the Type II error rate. Moving the line to the right reduces the significance level (e.g., α 0.05 to 0.01), which decreases the Type I error rate but increases the type II error rate.

Is One Error Worse Than the Other?

As you've seen, the nature of the two types of error, their causes, and the certainty of their rates of occurrence are all very different.

A common question is whether one type of error is worse than the other? Statisticians designed hypothesis tests to control Type I errors while Type II errors are much less defined. Consequently, many statisticians state that it is better to fail to detect an effect when it exists than to conclude an effect exists when it doesn't. In other words, there is a tendency to assume that Type I errors are worse.

However, reality is more complicated than that. You should carefully consider the consequences of each type of error for your specific test.

Suppose you are assessing the strength of a new jet engine part that is under consideration. People's lives are riding on the part's strength. A false negative in this scenario merely means that the part is strong enough, but the test fails to detect it. This outcome does not put anyone's life at risk. On the other hand, Type I errors are worse in this situation because they indicate the part is strong enough when it is not.

Now suppose that the jet engine part is already in use, but there are concerns about it failing. In this case, you want the test to be more sensitive to detecting problems even at the risk of false positives. Type II errors are worse in this scenario because the test fails to detect the problem and leave these problematic parts in use for longer.

Using hypothesis tests effectively requires that you understand their error rates. By setting the significance level and estimating your test's power, you can manage both error rates so they meet your requirements.

In the next section, we'll focus on power analysis, a critical process for managing Type II errors before you begin collecting data.

Power and Sample Size Analysis

Statistical power is the opposite of Type II errors, both mathematically $(1 - \beta)$ and conceptually. Power is the ability of the test to detect an effect that exists in the population. In other words, the test correctly rejects a false null hypothesis.

For example, if your study has 80% power, it has an 80% chance of detecting an effect that exists. Let this point be a reminder that when you work with samples, nothing is guaranteed! When an effect exists in the population, your study might not detect it because you are working with a sample. Samples contain sample error, which can occasionally cause a random sample to misrepresent the population.

80% power is a standard benchmark for studies. However, you'll need to consider standards for your field or industry.

As you learned in the previous sections, while various factors affect power, researchers have the greatest control over sample size.

Determining a good sample size for a study is always an important issue. After all, using the wrong sample size can doom your study from the start. Fortunately, power analysis can find the answer for you. Power analysis combines statistical analysis, subject-area knowledge, and your requirements to help you derive the optimal sample size.

As you'll see in this section, both under-powered and over-powered studies are problematic. Let's learn how to find the right sample size for your study!

Before data collection and hypothesis testing begin, you must do a lot of preplanning. This planning includes identifying the data you will gather, how you will collect it, and how you will measure it, among many other details. A crucial part of the planning is determining how much data you need to collect. I'll show you how to estimate the sample size for your study.

Before we get to estimating sample size requirements, let's review the factors that influence statistical significance. This process will help you see the value of formally going through a power and sample size analysis rather than guessing.

Factors Involved in Statistical Significance

Look at the chart below and identify which study found a real treatment effect and which one didn't. Within each study, the difference between the treatment group and the control group is the sample estimate of the effect size.

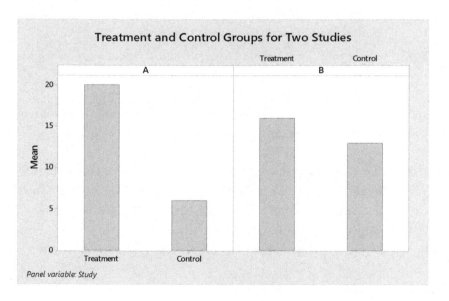

Did either study obtain significant results? The estimated effects in both studies can represent either a real effect or random sample error.

You don't have enough information to make that determination. Hypothesis tests incorporate these considerations to determine whether the results are statistically significant.

- **Effect size**: The larger the effect size, the less likely it is to be random error. It's clear that Study A exhibits a more substantial effect in the sample—but that's insufficient by itself.
- **Sample size**: Larger sample sizes allow hypothesis tests to detect smaller effects. If Study B's sample size is large enough, its more modest effect can be statistically significant.
- **Variability**: When your sample data have more variability, random sampling error is more likely to produce considerable differences between the experimental groups even when there is no real effect. If the sample data in Study A have sufficient variability, random error might be responsible for the large difference.

Hypothesis testing takes all this information and uses it to calculate the p-value—which you use to determine statistical significance. The key takeaway is that the statistical significance of any effect depends collectively on the size of the effect, the sample size, and the variability present in the sample data. Consequently, you cannot determine the right sample size in a vacuum because the three factors are intertwined.

Goals of a Power Analysis

Power analysis involves taking these three considerations, adding subject-area knowledge, and managing tradeoffs to settle on a sample size. During this process, you must rely heavily on your expertise to provide reasonable estimates of the input values.

Power analysis helps you manage an essential tradeoff. As you increase the sample size, the hypothesis test gains a greater ability to detect small effects. This situation sounds fantastic. However, larger sample sizes cost more money. And, there is a point where an effect becomes so miniscule that it is meaningless in a practical sense.

You don't want to collect a large and expensive sample only to be able to detect an effect that is too small to be useful! Nor do you want an underpowered study that has a low probability of detecting a vital effect. Your goal is to collect a large enough sample to have sufficient power to detect a meaningful effect—but not too large to be wasteful.

As you'll see in the upcoming examples, the analyst provides numeric values that correspond to "a good chance" and "meaningful effect." These values allow you to tailor the analysis to your needs.

All these details might sound complicated, but a statistical power analysis helps you manage them. In fact, going through this procedure forces you to focus on the relevant information. Typically, you specify three factors and your statistical software calculates the remaining value. For instance, if you specify the smallest effect size that is practically significant, variability, and power, the software calculates the required sample size.

Let's work through an example to bring this to life.

2-Sample t-Test Power Analysis for Sample Size

Suppose we're conducting a 2-sample t-test to determine which of two materials is stronger. If one material is significantly stronger than the other, we'll use that material in our process. Furthermore, we've tested these materials in a pilot study, which provides background knowledge for the estimates.

In a power and sample size analysis, statistical software presents you with a dialog box something like the following:

Power and Sample Size for 2-Sample t

Specify values for any two of the following:

Sample sizes:

Differences: 5

Power values: .9

Standard deviation: 4

Options...   Graph...

Help   OK   Cancel

We'll go through these fields one-by-one. First off, we will leave **Sample sizes** blank because we want the software to calculate this value.

Differences

Differences is often a confusing value to enter. Do not enter your guess for the difference between the two types of material. Instead, use your expertise to identify the smallest difference that is still meaningful for your application. In other words, you consider smaller differences to be inconsequential. It would not be worthwhile to expend resources to detect them.

By choosing this value carefully, you tailor the experiment so that it has a reasonable chance of detecting useful differences while allowing smaller, non-useful differences to remain potentially undetected. This value helps prevent us from collecting an unnecessarily large sample.

For our example, we'll enter 5 because smaller differences are unimportant for our process.

Power values

Power values is where we specify the probability that the hypothesis test detects the difference in the sample if that difference exists in the population. This field is where you define the "reasonable chance" that I mentioned earlier. If you hold the other input values constant and increase the test's power, the required sample size also increases. The proper value to enter in this field depends on norms in your study area or industry. Common power values are 0.8 and 0.9.

We'll enter a power of 0.9 so that the 2-sample t-test has a 90% chance of detecting a difference of 5.

Standard deviation

Standard deviation is the field where we enter the data variability. We need to enter an estimate for the standard deviation of material strength. Analysts frequently base these estimates on pilot studies and historical research data. Inputting better variability estimates will produce more reliable power analysis results. Consequently, you should strive to improve these estimates over time as you perform additional studies and testing. Providing reasonable estimates of the standard deviation is often the most challenging part of a power and sample size analysis.

For our example, we'll assume that the two types of material have a standard deviation of 4 units of strength. After we click OK, we see the results.

Interpreting the Power Analysis Results

Power analysis provides both numeric and graphical results, as shown on the next page.

Power and Sample Size

```
2-Sample t Test

Testing mean 1 = mean 2 (versus ≠)
Calculating power for mean 1 = mean 2 + difference
α = 0.05  Assumed standard deviation = 4

                Sample   Target
Difference       Size    Power    Actual Power
         5         15     0.9         0.910482

The sample size is for each group.
```

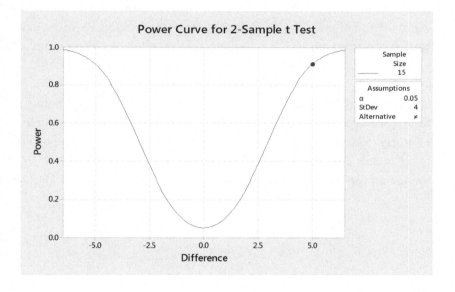

The text output indicates that we need 15 samples per group (total of 30) to have a 90% chance of detecting a difference of 5 units.

The dot on the Power Curve corresponds to the information in the text output. However, by studying the entire graph, we can learn additional information about how statistical power varies by the difference. If we start at the dot and move down the curve to a difference of 2.5, we learn the test has a power of approximately 0.4 (40%). This power is too low. However, we indicated that differences less than 5 were not practically significant to our process. Consequently, having a low ability to detect a difference of 2.5 is not problematic.

119

Conversely, follow the curve up from the dot and notice how power quickly increases to nearly 100% before reaching a difference of 6. This design satisfies the process requirements while using a manageable sample size of 15 per group.

Calculating Power Using Standardized Effects

In the previous example, I had to enter the difference and the standard deviation in the software. You can think of the difference as the raw effect. However, other statistical software require you to enter a standardized effect. I'll redo the previous example using a free power calculation program called G*Power, which requires you to enter a Cohen's d effect size for t-tests. I highly recommend this program.

Cohen's d is the standardized effect for means. It is simply the mean difference divided by the standard deviation. In the previous example, I entered a difference of 5 and a standard deviation of 4. That equates to a Cohen's d of 5 / 4 = 1.25. In G*Power, I enter the equivalent information for the previous example.

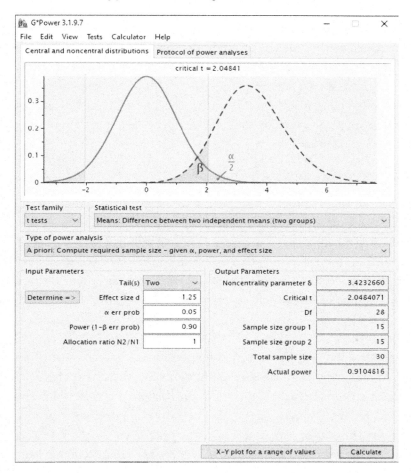

The input parameters are the values I enter. The results are in the output parameters. Unsurprisingly, we get the same group sizes and power results. G*Power even includes a nice graph at the top that illustrates your power analysis. It's similar to the error rate graph I presented earlier in this chapter.

Other types of statistical tests have different measures for standardized effects. You just have to know how to convert from the raw effect (difference) to the standardized effect, as we did for Cohen's d.

Even if you're not sure what raw effect to expect for your study, you might have a general idea of whether it is small, medium, or large. Researchers have developed a consensus for standardized effects that relate to these sizes. Consequently, one benefit of using standardized effects is that you can enter a standardized value (which G*Power provides) for small, medium, or large rather than estimating both the raw effect size and variability.

Use Power Analysis for All Studies

Throughout this section, we've been looking at continuous data and using the 2-sample t-test to compare means. For continuous data, you can also use power analysis to assess sample sizes for ANOVA designs. Additionally, there are hypothesis tests for other types of data, such as proportions tests (binomial data) and rates of occurrence (Poisson data). These tests have their corresponding power and sample analyses.

In general, when you move away from continuous data to these other types of data, your sample size requirements increase. And, there are unique intricacies in each. For instance, in a proportions test, you need a relatively larger sample size to detect a difference when your proportion is closer 0 or 1 than if it is in the middle (0.5). Many factors can affect the optimal sample size. Power analysis helps you navigate these concerns.

After reading this section, I hope you see how power analysis combines statistical analyses, subject-area knowledge, and your requirements to help you derive the optimal sample size for your specific needs. If you don't perform this analysis, you risk conducting a study that is either likely to miss an important effect or have an exorbitantly large sample size.

Finally, experimentation is an iterative process. As you conduct more studies in an area, you'll develop better estimates to input into power and sample size analyses and gain a clearer picture of how to proceed.

Low Power Tests Exaggerate Effect Sizes

I'm going to end this chapter with an advanced topic about statistical power. The previous sections of this chapter have shown you that a study with low power is unlikely to detect an effect when it exists. However, there is an additional danger to consider with low powered studies.

Clearly, a high-powered study is a good thing just for being able to identify these effects. Low power reduces your chances of discovering real findings. However, many analysts don't realize that low power also tends to exaggerate the effect size when they detect effects.

In this section, I show how this unexpected relationship between power and exaggerated effect sizes exists. I'll also tie it to other issues, such as the bias of effects published in journals and other matters about statistical power. I think this topic will be eye-opening and thought provoking! As always, I'll use many graphs rather than equations.

Hypothetical Study Scenario

To illustrate how this effect size inflation works, I'll simulate a study and conduct it many times at three power levels.

Imagine that we're studying a fictitious medication that promises to increase your intelligence (IQ). Our experiment has two groups—a control group that doesn't take the pill and the treatment group that does. Then, each group takes the same IQ test and we compare the results. The effect size is the difference between group means.

Because we're simulating these studies, we can control the effect size and other properties of the population. I'll set the effect size at 10 IQ points and define the two populations as follows:

- **Control group**: Normal distribution with a mean of 100 and a standard deviation of 15.
- **Treatment group**: Normal distribution with a mean of 110 and a standard deviation of 15.

I calculated the sample sizes I need to produce statistical power of 0.3, 0.55, and 0.8. The first two values represent low power studies, while the third value is a standard target value. The output below shows the power analysis results.

```
Power and Sample Size

2-Sample t Test

Testing mean 1 = mean 2 (versus ≠)
Calculating power for mean 1 = mean 2 + difference
α = 0.05   Assumed standard deviation = 15

               Sample   Target
Difference     Size     Power     Actual Power
        10       11      0.30         0.319006
        10       21      0.55         0.558951
        10       37      0.80         0.807587

The sample size is for each group.
```

Now, I'll use statistical software to draw 50 random samples from the two populations for each of the sample sizes in the power analysis. Finally, I perform 2-sample t-tests on all datasets. I use two-tailed tests with a significance level of 0.05. The following discussion explains the results of the 50 2-sample t-tests for each of the three power levels.

Findings and Estimated Effect Sizes for Very Low Power (0.3)

We know that the correct effect size for these analyses is 10. Let's see what the 2-sample hypothesis tests reveal for the 50 datasets that have a power of 0.3. Given this power, we expect to detect the effect 30%

of the time. We'd expect that percentage if we perform the test an infinite number of times. However, we conducted it only 50 times, so there's a margin of error around the percentage of significant studies.

Of the 50 tests with the lowest statistical power, 13 (26%) are statistically significant. The average effect size is 17.05 IQ points, and the range extends from 12.01 to 21.45. Not only is the average effect too high, but the entire range of effects is greater than the actual effect. The graph below displays the distribution of statistically significant findings with a reference line for the real effect (10).

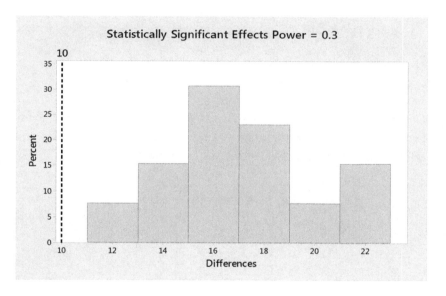

Now, let's look at the results for the other two levels of statistical power.

Power = 0.55

Of the 50 tests, 34 (68%) are statistically significant. The average effect size is 13.50, and the range extends from 7.71 to 19.04. A large majority of the effects are greater than 10.

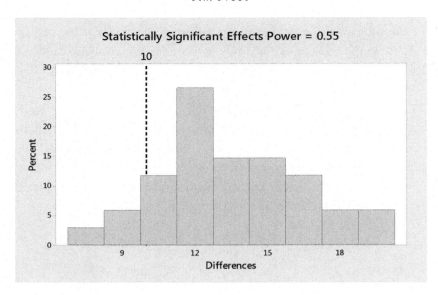

Power = 0.8

Of the 50 tests, 41 (82%) are statistically significant. The average effect size is 11.92, and the range extends from 6.30 to 19.43. The real effect size is moving closer to the center of the distribution.

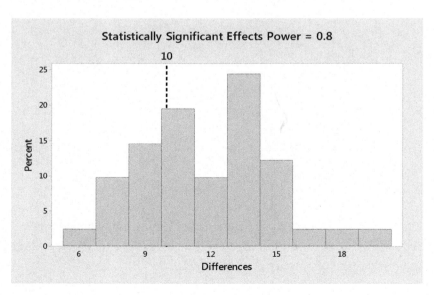

Relationship between Statistical Power and Effect Size

As the power level increases, the percentage of detections increases and the exaggeration of the effect size decreases. Both are good things and have a common cause. The graph below displays the exaggeration factor (mean significant effect / actual effect) by power. No exaggeration occurs at a value of one.

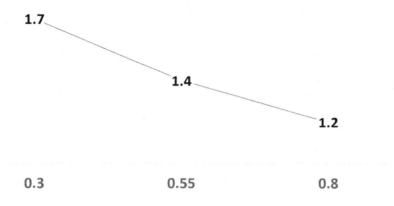

EXAGGERATION FACTOR BY POWER

We saw that the effects all have a positive bias amongst the statistically significant studies. Typically, researchers and peer-reviewed journals pay attention only to statistically significant findings. After all, insignificant results indicate that your sample provides insufficient evidence to conclude that the effect exists in the population. But, let's look at all the outcomes, both significant and non-significant, for the three power levels.

For each of the three power levels, all 50 tests have an average effect near the correct value of 10. Additionally, the effects are symmetrically distributed around 10 approximately.

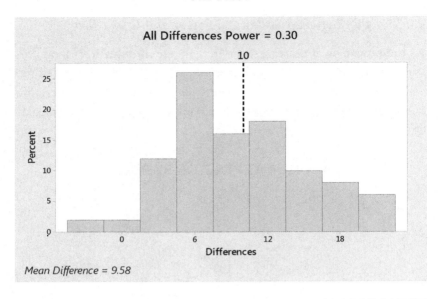

Mean Difference = 9.58

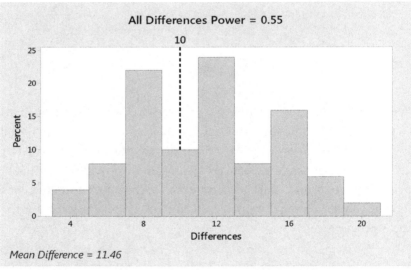

Mean Difference = 11.46

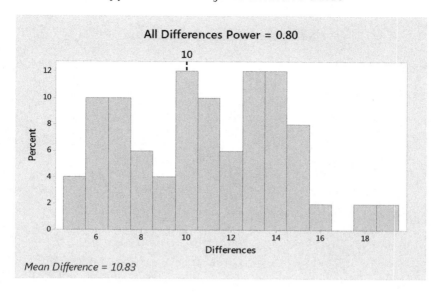

Mean Difference = 10.83

Clue: When we assess both the significant and non-significant studies together, the estimated effect is an unbiased estimator of the actual population effect. However, when we evaluate only the statistically significant results, the estimated effect is a biased estimator.

Let's graph the distribution of significant and non-significant to explore this clue.

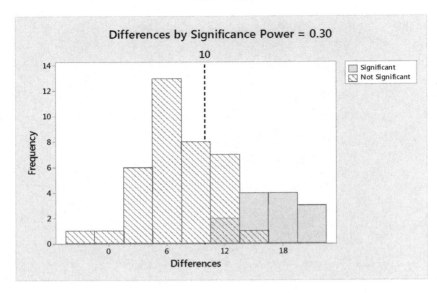

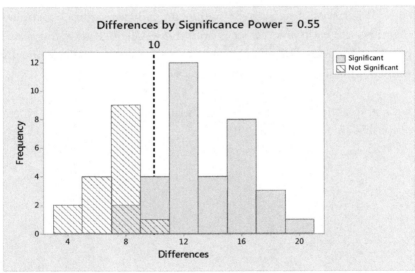

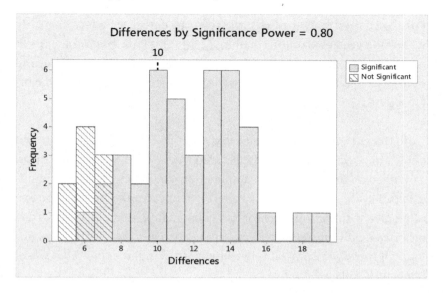

These graphs show that the hypothesis test classifies the most extreme effect sizes as being statistically significant. As the power level increases, more moderate effect sizes become significant. That's precisely how hypothesis tests are supposed to work!

How Low Statistical Power Biases the Estimates

We noticed that those full distributions of both significant and nonsignificant test results approximately center on the correct effect size. However, that was not true with biased estimates of the significant findings.

For a value to be the mean of a symmetric distribution, it must have roughly an equal number of values above and below it. In this case, we know the correct effect size is 10. However, statistical power affects how extreme an estimated effect size must be for the test to classify it as statistically significant. The non-significant findings are systematically on the low end of the distribution. By filtering the results by statistical significance, you exclude these smaller effects when calculating the mean, which biases the mean upwards.

For a statistical power of 0.3, the test can detect an effect size only when it is greater than or equal to 13.39 IQ points given the experimental conditions. I calculated this value using the critical t-value and multiplying it by the standard error of the differences between means (2.093 * 6.396).

Note that 13.39 is greater than the correct effect size of 10. From that value alone, you know the significant effects will be biased upwards. You need an unusually high sample effect to obtain statistical significance. This high critical value severely truncates the full distribution of results, which eliminates the lower estimates (i.e., < 10) that would otherwise pull the average down to the correct value. It also explains why all the significant sample estimates are greater than 10. Consequently, it's biased too high.

The minimum detectable effects size for powers of 0.55 and 0.8 are 9.14 and 6.95, respectively. These higher-powered tests can detect less extreme effect sizes. However, it still truncates the lower end of the distribution, which biases the effects upward. The only way to avoid this type of bias is to have a statistical power of 100%, which includes all the test results. However, hypothesis tests never obtain 100% power. Fortunately, when you're near 80% power, the bias is relatively small.

Graphical Representation

The upcoming charts show how this works using probability distribution plots for a power of 0.3 and 0.8. The dashed distribution on the left is the t-distribution that the 2-sample t-test uses to determine statistical significance given the design. The 0 and the CV value at the top correspond to the t-distribution. They pinpoint the null hypothesis value (difference = 0) and the upper critical value (CV) for a two-tailed test. I don't display the lower critical value. For convenience, I've converted the t-values you usually see with t-distributions to the real data units.

The distribution on the right with the solid line is the expected distribution of differences between means given the properties of the two populations. This distribution represents the alternative hypothesis. In practice, you will never know its precise properties. The number 10 locates the mean IQ difference associated with the correct effect, which occurs at the peak of the solid line curve.

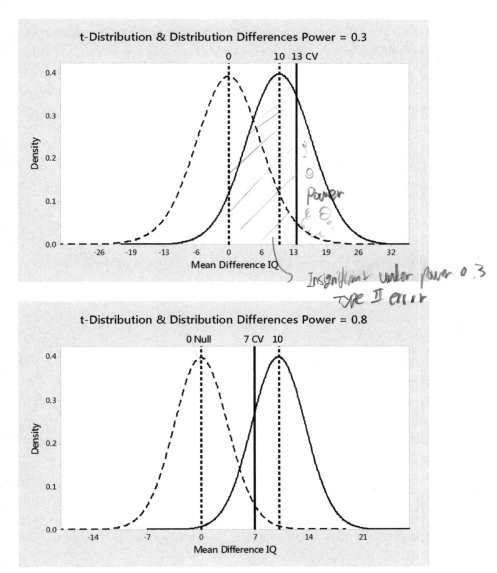

Here are some essential aspects to notice.

Notice how the critical value line truncates the distribution of differences in the alternative hypothesis (solid line) curves on the right. All differences on the solid line curve to the left of the CV line will not be significant. This portion of the solid line curve represents false negatives—type II errors. Consequently, those smaller effect sizes won't be included in the calculations for the mean of the significant effect sizes. The average effect must be higher than the critical value. Truncation diminishes as power increases from 0.3 to 0.8. The amount of truncation determines the degree of bias in the estimated effect amongst statistically significant results.

The area under the solid curve to the right of the CV line represents the test's power because those differences will be significant. For 0.3 statistical power, 30% of the area under the solid curve is to the right of the CV line. For 0.8 power, 80% is to the right of the CV line.

Higher proportions of the solid curve to the right of the CV line corresponds to a lower bias of significant effects and greater statistical power.

Discussion

I hope this illustration was an eye-opener. I suspect the fact that low power studies inflate effect sizes is underappreciated. Typically, analysts think the biggest danger of low power studies is missing an effect, which is a real possibility. However, when an analyst obtains significant results with low power, they are relieved, but they don't realize it inflates the effect size!

Particular fields are more prone to conducting studies with small sample sizes and low power. For example, psychology studies routinely use small samples. Unsurprisingly, psychology has had problems with exaggerated effect sizes. Alternatively, researchers might use a small pilot study to start, which could produce inflated effect sizes.

You might have heard that effect sizes in journal articles are biased because editors publish only significant studies. While the articles in a journal won't all neatly have the same power, the same principle applies. By restricting publication by p-values, journals exclude the smaller estimates.

Imagine you're researching a subject area and you find all published articles about a particular effect. You might think that by averaging them together, you'll get a reasonable estimate. That's not necessarily the case! Think back to the first set of graphs that displayed only the significant results. Those were biased. It wasn't until we added in all the smaller, non-significant effects that the average effect was close to the actual effect.

Finally, calculating power for this simulation was easy because I knew the correct values to enter into the power calculations. However, for a study in the real-world, it can be difficult. Consequently, you might not always realize you have a low power study. Consider that the smallest studies in these simulations had 22 subjects split between two groups, which produced a statistical power of 0.3. If this were a real study, I bet the researchers would not realize it had such low power.

When in doubt, err on the size of larger sample sizes. And, do your best to be realistic with the power calculations!

Review and Next Steps

In this chapter, we discussed the four possible outcomes of a hypothesis test and focused on the two types of errors:

Type I: Reject a true null hypothesis. This is a false positive because the effect does not exist in the population, but the p-value for the sample tells you to reject the null.

Type II: Fail to reject a false null hypothesis. This is a false negative because the effect exists in the population, but the p-value for the sample indicates that you should fail to reject the null.

If you're looking for a mnemonic way to remember what each error represents, the only one I know is to mentally link the homonyms in Type "two" and "fail *to* reject." It's not the best, but it worked for me as a student!

Typically, you won't know for sure when either error occurs. However, statistical tools can help you manage both types of error rates.

The Type I error rate equals the significance level, which is also known as alpha (α). Managing Type I errors is simple. Just set the significance level to your desired Type I error rate.

The Type II error rate is also known as beta (β). However, managing the Type II error rate is more complex because it involves estimating properties of the hypothesized distribution for the alternative hypothesis. These properties are seldom known, and you'll need to rely on educated guesses. Analysts try to increase statistical power, which is $1 - \beta$. Therefore, increasing power will decrease the Type II error rate.

In the next chapter, you'll learn about the differences between one-tailed and two-tailed hypothesis tests, which refers to the tails of the sampling distributions. Some hypothesis tests, such as t-tests, have two forms of the test. You'll learn about when you need to choose between one- and two-tailed tests and how to make that decision.

CHAPTER 6

One-Tailed and Two-Tailed Hypothesis Tests

While this book so far has focused on comparing means using t-tests, I start transitioning to other types of tests in this chapter. I bring in these additional tests because the need to perform one-tailed and two-tailed tests vary by the kind of test. In this chapter, I just touch on these other tests. Later chapters go into them in much more detail.

Hypothesis tests use test statistics and their sampling distributions, such as the t-distribution, F-distribution, and chi-squared distribution. These distributions display the probabilities of obtaining test statistic values when the null hypothesis is correct.

On a probability distribution plot, the portion of the shaded area under the curve represents the probability that a value will fall within that range.

The following graph displays a sampling distribution for t-values. The two shaded regions cover critical regions in the two-tails of the distribution. Unsurprisingly, this corresponds to a two-tailed test. And, you guessed it, a hypothesis test with a critical region in just one tail is a one-tailed hypothesis test.

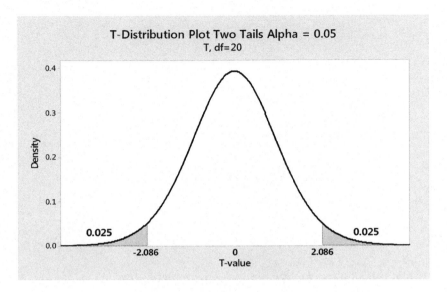

Choosing whether to perform a one-tailed or a two-tailed hypothesis test is one of the methodology decisions you might need to make for your analysis. This choice can have critical implications for the effects it can detect, statistical power, and potential errors.

In this section, you'll learn about the differences between one-tailed and two-tailed hypothesis tests and their advantages and disadvantages.

Critical Regions

In hypothesis tests, critical regions are ranges of the distributions where the values represent statistically significant results. Analysts define the size and location of the critical regions by specifying both the significance level (alpha) and whether the test is one-tailed or two-tailed.

Consider the following two facts:

- The significance level is the probability of rejecting a correct null hypothesis.
- The sampling distribution for a test statistic assumes that the null hypothesis is correct.

Consequently, to represent the critical regions on the distribution for a test statistic, you merely shade the appropriate percentage of the distribution. For the typical significance level of 0.05, you shade 5% of the distribution.

Two-Tailed Tests

Two-tailed hypothesis tests are also known as nondirectional and two-sided tests because you can test for effects in both directions. When you perform a two-tailed test, you split the significance level percentage between both tails of the distribution. In the example below, I use an alpha of 5% and the distribution has two shaded regions of 2.5% (2 * 2.5% = 5%).

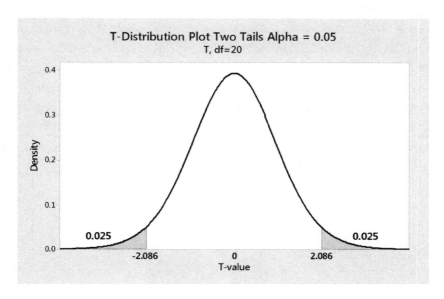

When a test statistic falls in either critical region, your sample data are sufficiently incompatible with the null hypothesis that you can reject it for the population.

In a two-tailed test, the generic null and alternative hypotheses are the following:

- **Null**: The effect equals zero.
- **Alternative**: The effect does not equal zero.

The specifics of the effect depend on the type of test you perform because you might be assessing means, proportions, or rates.

Example of a two-tailed 1-sample t-test

Suppose we perform a two-sided 1-sample t-test where we compare the mean strength (4.1) of parts from a supplier to a target value (5). We use a two-tailed test because we care whether the mean is greater than or less than the target value.

To interpret the results, simply compare the p-value to your significance level. If the p-value is less than the significance level, you know that the test statistic fell into one of the critical regions, but which one?

Just look at the estimated effect. In the output below, the t-value is negative, so we know that the test statistic falls in the critical region in the left tail of the distribution, indicating the mean is less than the target value. Now we know this difference is statistically significant.

One-Sample T: Two-Tailed

Test of $\mu = 5$ vs $\neq 5$

N	Mean	StDev	SE Mean	95% CI	T	P
21	4.100	1.600	0.349	(3.372, 4.828)	-2.58	0.018

We can conclude that the population mean for part strength is less than the target value. However, the test had the capacity to detect a positive difference as well. You can also assess the confidence interval. With a two-tailed hypothesis test, you obtain a two-sided confidence interval. The confidence interval tells us that the population mean is likely to fall between 3.372 and 4.828. This range excludes the target value (5), which is another indicator of significance.

Advantages of two-tailed hypothesis tests

You can detect both positive and negative effects. Two-tailed tests are standard in scientific research where discovering any type of effect is usually of interest to researchers.

One-Tailed Tests

One-tailed hypothesis tests are also known as directional and one-sided tests because you can test for effects in only one direction. When you perform a one-tailed test, the entire significance level percentage goes into one tail of the distribution.

In the upcoming examples, I use an alpha of 5%. Each distribution has one shaded region of 5%. When you perform a one-tailed analysis, you must determine whether the critical region is in the left tail or the right tail. The test can detect an effect only in the direction that has the critical region. It has absolutely no capacity to detect an effect in the other direction.

In a one-tailed test, you have two options for the null and alternative hypotheses, which corresponds to where you place the critical region.

You can choose either of the following sets of generic hypotheses:

- **Null**: The effect is less than or equal to zero.
- **Alternative**: The effect is greater than zero.

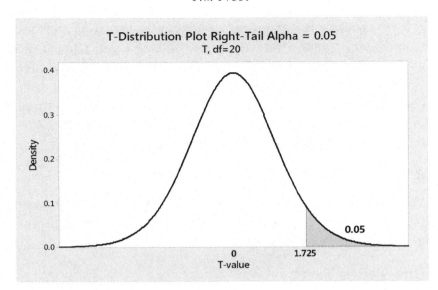

Or:

- **Null**: The effect is greater than or equal to zero.
- **Alternative**: The effect is less than zero.

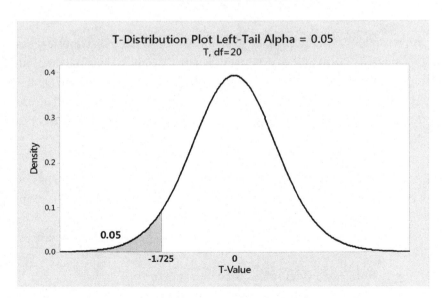

Again, the specifics of the effect depend on the type of test you perform.

Notice how for both possible null hypotheses the tests can't distinguish between zero and an effect in a particular direction. For example, in the previous example, the null combines "the effect is greater than or equal to zero" into a single category. That test can't differentiate between zero and greater than zero. It can detect only negative effects.

Example of a one-tailed 1-sample t-test

Suppose we perform a one-tailed 1-sample t-test. We'll use a similar scenario as before, where we compare the mean strength of parts from a supplier (102) to a target value (100). Imagine we are considering a new parts supplier and will use them only if their parts' mean strength is greater than our target value. We don't need to differentiate between whether their parts are equally strong or less strong than the target because, either way, we'd just stick with our current supplier.

Consequently, we'll choose the alternative hypothesis that states the mean difference is greater than zero (Population mean − Target value > 0). The null hypothesis states that the difference between the population mean and target value is less than or equal to zero.

One-Sample T: One-Tailed

Test of $\mu = 100$ vs > 100

N	Mean	StDev	SE Mean	95% Lower Bound	T	P
25	102.000	4.000	0.800	100.631	2.50	0.010

To interpret the results, compare the p-value to your significance level. If the p-value is less than the significance level, you know that the test statistic falls within the critical region. For this study, the statistically significant result supports the notion that the population mean is greater than the target value of 100.

Confidence intervals for a one-tailed test are similarly one-sided. You obtain either an upper bound or a lower bound. In this case, we get a lower bound, which indicates that the population mean is likely to be greater than or equal to 100.631. There is no upper limit to this range.

Obtaining a lower-bound matches our goal of determining whether the new parts are stronger than our target value. The fact that the lower bound (100.631) is higher than the target value (100) indicates that these results are statistically significant.

The test in our example cannot detect a negative difference even when the sample mean represents a very negative effect.

Advantages and disadvantages of one-tailed hypothesis tests

One-tailed tests have more statistical power to detect an effect in one direction than a two-tailed test with the same design and significance level. One-tailed tests occur most frequently for studies where one of the following is true:

- Effects can exist in only one direction.
- Effects can exist in both directions, but the researchers only care about an effect in one direction. There is no drawback to failing to detect an effect in the other direction. (Not recommended.)

The disadvantage of one-tailed tests is that they have no statistical power to detect an effect in the other direction.

As part of your pre-study planning process, determine whether you'll use the one- or two-tailed version of a hypothesis test.

This section explains the differences between one-tailed and two-tailed hypothesis tests. While the methodology behind how these two forms of hypothesis tests function is clear from a mathematical standpoint, there is some debate about when it is appropriate to use one-tailed tests. The next section explores this decision.

When Can I Use One-Tailed Tests?

One-tailed hypothesis tests offer the promise of more statistical power compared to an equivalent two-tailed design. While there is some debate about when you can use a one-tailed test, the consensus among statisticians is that you should use two-tailed tests unless you have concrete reasons for using a one-tailed test.

In this section, I discuss when you should and should not use one-tailed tests. I'll cover the different schools of thought and offer my opinion.

Two-Tailed Tests are the Default Choice

The vast majority of hypothesis tests that analysts perform are two-tailed because they can detect effects in both directions. This fact is generally the clincher. In most studies, you are interested in determining whether there is a positive effect or negative effect. In other words, results in either direction provide meaningful information. If this statement describes your study, you must use a two-tailed test. Typically, you need a strong reason to move away from using two-tailed tests.

On the other hand, there are some cases where one-tailed tests are not only a valid option, but truly are a requirement.

Consequently, there is a spectrum that ranges from cases where one-tailed tests are not appropriate to situations where they are required. In the middle of this spectrum, there are cases where analysts might disagree. The breadth of opinions extends from those who believe you should use one-tailed tests for only a few specific situations when they are required to those who are more lenient about their usage.

A Concrete Rule about Choosing Between One- and Two-Tailed Tests

Despite this disagreement, there is a hard and fast rule about the decision process itself upon which all statisticians agree. You must decide whether you will use a one-tailed or two-tailed test at the beginning of your study before you look at your data. You must not perform a two-tailed analysis, obtain non-significant results, and then try a one-tailed test to see if that is statistically significant. If you plan to use a one-tailed test, make this decision at the beginning of the study and explain why it is the proper choice.

The approach I'll take is to assume you'll use a two-tailed test and then move away from that only after carefully determining that a one-tailed test is appropriate for your study. The following are potential reasons for why you might use a one-tailed hypothesis test.

One-Tailed Tests Can Be the Only Option

For some hypothesis tests, the mechanics of how a test functions dictate using a one-tailed methodology. Chi-squared tests and F-tests and are often one-tailed for this reason.

Chi-squared tests

Analysts often use chi-squared tests to determine whether data fit a theoretical distribution and whether categorical variables are independent. For these tests, when the chi-squared value exceeds the critical threshold, you have sufficient evidence to conclude that the data do not follow the distribution or that the categorical variables are dependent. The chi-squared value either reaches this threshold or it does not.

For all values below the threshold, you fail to reject the null hypothesis. There is no other interpretation for very low chi-squared values. Hence, these tests are one-tailed by their nature.

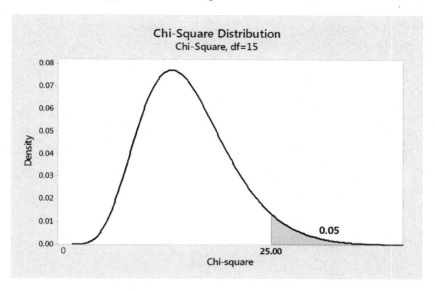

F-tests

F-tests are highly flexible tests that analysts use in a wide variety of scenarios. Some of these scenarios exclude the possibility of a two-tailed test. For instance, F-tests in ANOVA are like the chi-squared example. The F ratio can increase to the significance threshold or it does not. In one-way ANOVA, if the F-value surpasses the threshold, you can conclude that not all group means are equal.

On the other hand, all F-values below the threshold yield the same interpretation—the sample provides insufficient evidence to conclude that the group means are unequal. No other effect or interpretation exists for very low F-values.

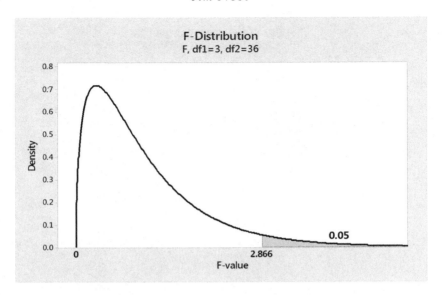

When a one-tailed version of the test is the only meaningful possibility, statistical software won't ask you to choose. That's why you'll never need to choose between a one or two-tailed ANOVA F-test or chi-square tests.

In some cases, the nature of the test itself requires using a one-sided methodology, and it does not depend on the study area.

Effects can Occur in Only One Direction

On the other hand, other hypothesis tests can legitimately have one and two-tailed versions, and you need to choose between them based on the study area. Tests that fall in this category include t-tests, proportion tests, Poisson rate tests, variance tests, and some nonparametric tests for the median. In these cases, base the decision on subject-area knowledge about the possible effects.

For some study areas, the effect can exist in only one direction. It simply can't exist in the other direction. To make this determination, you need to use your subject-area knowledge and understanding of physical limitations. In this case, if there were a difference in the untested direction, you would attribute it to random error regardless of how large it is. In other words, only chance can produce an observed effect in the other direction. If you have even the smallest notion that an observed effect in the other direction could be a real effect rather than random error, use a two-tailed test.

For example, imagine we are comparing an herbicide's ability to kill weeds to no treatment. We randomly apply the herbicide to some patches of grass and no herbicide to other patches. It is inconceivable that the herbicide can promote weed growth. In the worst-case scenario, it is entirely ineffective, and the herbicide patches should be equivalent to the control group. If the herbicide patches ultimately have more weeds than the control group, we'll chalk that up to random error regardless of the difference—even if it's substantial. In this case, we are wholly justified using a one-tailed test to determine whether the herbicide is better than no treatment.

No Controversy So Far!

The preceding two reasons fall entirely on safe ground. Using one-tailed tests because of its mechanics or because an effect can occur in only one direction should be acceptable to all statisticians. In fact, some statisticians believe that these are the only valid reasons for using one-tailed hypothesis tests. I happen to fall within this school of thought myself.

In the next section, I'll discuss a scenario where some analysts believe you can choose between one and two-tailed tests, but others disagree with that notion.

Only Need to Detect Effects in One Direction

In this scenario, effects can exist in both directions, but you only care about detecting an effect in one direction. Analysts use the one-tailed approach in this situation to boost the statistical power of the hypothesis test.

To even consider using a one-tailed test for this reason, you must be entirely sure there is no need to detect an effect in the other direction. While you gain more statistical power in one direction, the test has absolutely no power in the other direction.

Suppose you are testing a new vaccine and want to determine whether it's better than the current vaccine. You use a one-tailed test to improve the test's ability to learn whether the new vaccine is better. However, that's unethical because the test cannot determine whether it is less effective. You risk missing valuable information by testing in only one direction.

However, there might be occasions where you, or science, genuinely don't need to detect an effect in the untested direction. For example, suppose you are considering a new part that is cheaper than the current part. Your primary motivation for switching is the price reduction. The new part doesn't have to be better than the existing part, but it cannot be worse. In this case, it might be appropriate to perform a one-tailed test that determines whether the new part is worse than the old part. You won't know if it is better, but you don't need to know that.

As I mentioned, many statisticians don't think you should use a one-tailed test for this type of scenario. My position is that you should set up a two-tailed test that produces the same power benefits as a one-tailed test because that approach will accurately capture the underlying fact that effects can occur in both directions.

However, before explaining this alternate approach, I need to describe an additional problem with the this scenario.

Beware of the Power that One-Tailed Tests Provide

The promise of extra statistical power in the direction of interest is tempting. After all, if you don't care about effects in the opposite direction, what's the problem? It turns out there is an additional penalty that comes with the extra power.

Let's see why one-tailed tests are more powerful than two-tailed tests with the same significance level. The following graphs display t-distributions and critical t-values for two t-tests with the same sample size.

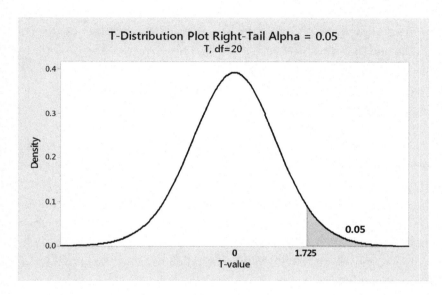

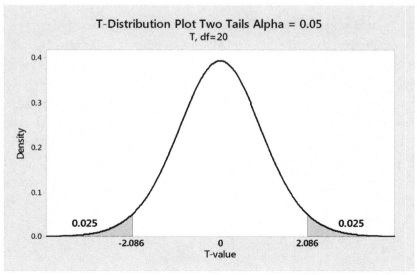

Notice how the one-tailed test requires a less extreme t-value (1.725) to produce a statistically significant result in the right tail than the two-tailed test (2.086). In other words, a smaller effect is statistically significant in the one-tailed analysis.

Both tests have the same Type I error rate because we defined the significance level as 0.05. This type of error occurs when the test rejects a true null hypothesis—a false positive. This error rate corresponds to the total percentage of the shaded areas under the curve. While both tests have the same overall Type I error rate, the distribution of these errors is different.

To understand why this occurs, keep in mind that the critical regions also represent where the Type I errors occur. For a two-tailed test, these errors are split equally between the left and right tails. However, for a one-tailed test, all these errors arise specifically in the one direction that you are interested in. Unfortunately, the error rate doubles in that direction compared to a two-tailed test. In the graphs, the right tail has an error rate of 5% in the one-tailed test compared to 2.5% in the two-tailed test.

By switching to a one-tailed test, you haven't changed anything of substance to gain this extra power. All you've done is to redraw the critical region so that a smaller effect in the direction of interest is statistically significant. In this light, it's not surprising that merely labeling smaller effects as being statistically significant also produces more false positives in that direction! And, the graphs reflect that fact.

If you want to increase the test's power without increasing the Type I error rate, you'll need to make a more fundamental change to your study's design, such as increasing your sample size or more effectively controlling the variability.

Is the Higher False Positive Rate Worthwhile?

To use a one-tailed test to gain more power, you can't care about detecting an effect in the other direction, and you have to be willing to accept twice the false positives in the direction you are interested. Remember, a false positive means that you will not obtain the benefits you expect.

Should you accept double the false positives in the direction of interest? Answering that question depends on the actions that a significant result will prompt. If you're considering changing to a new production line, that's a very costly decision. Doubling the false positives is problematic. Your company will spend a lot of money for a new manufacturing line, but it might not produce better products. However, if you're changing suppliers for a part based on the test result, and their parts don't cost more, a false positive isn't an expensive problem.

Think carefully about whether the additional power is worth the extra false positives in your direction of interest! If you decide that the added power is worth the risk, consider my alternative approach. It produces an equivalent amount of statistical power as the one-tailed approach. However, it uses a methodology that more accurately reflects the underlying reality of the study area and the goals of the analyst.

Alternative: Two-Tails with a Higher Alpha

In my view, determining the possible directions of an effect and the statistical power of the analysis are two independent issues. Using a one-tailed test to boost power can obscure these matters and their ramifications. My recommendation is to use the following process:

1. Identify the directions that an effect can occur, and then choose a one-tailed or two-tailed test accordingly.
2. Choose the significance level to correctly set the sensitivity and false-positive rate based on your specific requirements.

This process breaks down the questions you need to answer into two separate issues, which allows you to consider each more carefully.

Now, let's apply this process to the scenario where you're studying an effect that can occur in both directions, but the following are both true:

- You care about effects in only one direction.
- Increasing the power of the test is worth a higher risk of false positives in that direction.

In this situation, using a one-tailed test to gain extra power seems like an acceptable solution. However, that approach attempts to solve the right problem by using the wrong methodology. Here's my alternative method.

Instead of using a one-tailed test, consider using a two-tailed test and doubling the significance level, such as from 0.05 to 0.10. This approach increases your power while allowing the test methodology to match the reality of the situation better. It also increases the transparency of your goals as the analyst.

To understand this approach, compare the following graphs. The top chart is one-sided and uses a significance level of 0.05 while the bottom plot is two-sided and uses a significance level of 0.10.

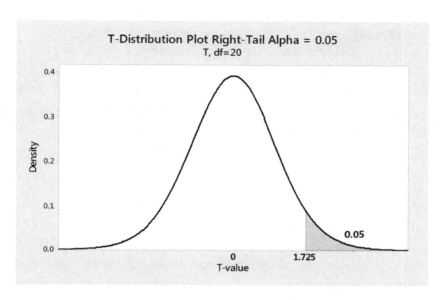

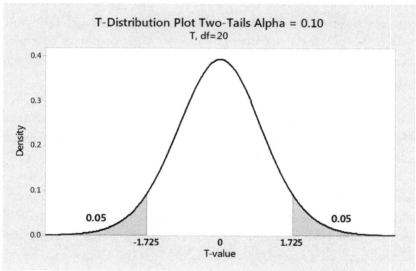

As you can see in the graphs, the critical region on the right side of both distributions starts at the same critical t-value (1.725). Consequently, both the one- and two-tailed tests provide the same power in that direction. Additionally, a critical region is present in the other tail, which means that the test can detect effects in the opposite direction as well.

The result is that the two-tailed test has the same power and an equal probability of a Type I error in the direction of interest. Great! And, you can detect effects in the other direction even though you might not need to know about them. Okay, that's not a bad thing.

This Approach Is More Transparent

What's so great about this approach? It makes your methodology choices more explicit while accurately reflecting a study area where effects can occur in both directions. Here's how.

The significance level is an evidentiary standard for the amount of sample evidence required to reject the null hypothesis. By increasing the significance level from 0.05 to 0.10, you're explicitly stating that you are lowering the amount of evidence necessary to reject the null, which logically increases the test's power. Additionally, as you raise the significance level, by definition the Type I error rate also increases.

This approach produces the same power gains as a one-tailed test. However, it more clearly indicates how the analyst set up a more sensitive test in exchange for a higher risk of false positives.

The problem with gaining the additional power by switching to a one-tailed test is that it obscures the fact that you're weakening the evidentiary standard. After all, you're not explicitly changing the significance level. That's why the increase in the Type I error rate in the direction of interest can be surprising!

Review and Next Steps

We covered a lot in this chapter. One- and two-tailed tests refer to the number of critical regions in a sampling distribution. Hypothesis tests can only detect effects where there are critical regions. Consequently, two-tailed tests can detect effects in both directions, while one-tailed tests can only detect effects in one direction.

If you use a significance level of 0.05, the critical region(s) will cover 5% of the sampling distribution. That 5% will either be all in one tail or split between two tails. Consequently, the single critical region in a one-tailed test covers twice the area under the curve as the corresponding critical region in a two-tailed test. One-tailed tests have more power to detect an effect in the direction of interest, but they also have twice the false positive rate in that direction.

For some tests, you need to choose between the one-tailed and two-tailed versions. When you need to decide, follow these guidelines. If the effect can occur in:

- One direction: Use a one-tailed test and choose the correct alternative hypothesis.
- Both directions: Use a two-tailed test.
- Both directions, but you care about only one direction and you need the higher statistical power: Use a two-tailed test and double the significance level. Be aware that you are doubling the probability of a false positive.

The next chapter covers several issues that relate to the importance of sample size. The first is degrees of freedom. You've seen statistical output display it as DF. We'll now explicitly define this to see how it affects several sampling distributions. The second is the central limit theorem.

CHAPTER 7

Sample Size
Considerations

This chapter covers several statistical concepts that relate to sample size. We'll start by exploring degrees of freedom, which we saw in action in chapter 3 with the sampling distributions for t-values. We'll see how degrees of freedom affect the sampling distributions of test statistics for other hypothesis tests.

Then we'll move on to the central limit theorem. You might recall that t-tests assume your data follow the normal distribution. However, you can waive this assumption if your sample is large enough. You can thank the central limit theorem!

Degrees of Freedom

In statistics, the degrees of freedom (DF) indicate the number of independent values that can vary in an analysis without breaking any constraints. It's related to sample size, but it's not directly equal to it. Degrees of freedom is an essential but slippery idea that appears in all parametric hypothesis tests. Learn how this fundamental concept affects the power and precision of your statistical analysis!

In this section, I bring this concept to life in an intuitive manner. I'll start by defining degrees of freedom. However, I'll quickly move on to practical examples in various contexts because they make this concept easier to understand.

Degrees of freedom are the number of independent values that a statistical analysis can estimate. You can also think of it as the number of values that are free to vary as you estimate parameters. I know, it's starting to sound a bit murky!

Degrees of freedom encompasses the notion that the amount of independent information you have limits the number of parameters that you can estimate. Typically, the degrees of freedom equal your sample size minus the number of parameters you need to calculate during an analysis. It is usually a positive whole number.

Degrees of freedom is a combination of how much data you have and how many parameters you need to estimate. It indicates how much independent information goes into a parameter estimate. In this vein, it's easy to see that you want a lot of information to go into parameter estimates to obtain more precise estimates and more powerful hypothesis tests. So, you want many degrees of freedom!

Independent Information and Constraints on Values

The definitions talk about independent information. You might think this refers to the sample size, but it's a little more complicated than that. To understand why, we need to talk about the freedom to vary. The best way to illustrate this concept is with an example.

Suppose we collect the following random sample of observations. Now, imagine that we know the mean, but we don't know the value of an observation—the X in the table.

Values

6
8
5
9
6
8
4
11
7
X

Average	6.9
Sum	69

The mean is 6.9, and it is based on 10 values. So, we know that the values must sum to 69 based on the equation for the mean.

Using simple algebra (64 + X = 69), we know that X must equal 5.

Estimating Parameters Imposes Constraints on the Data

As you can see, the last number has no freedom to vary. It is not an independent piece of information because it cannot be any other value. Estimating the parameter, the mean in this case, imposes a constraint on the freedom to vary. The last value and the mean are entirely dependent on each other. Consequently, after estimating the mean, we have only 9 independent pieces of information, even though our sample size is 10.

That's the basic idea for degrees of freedom in statistics. In a general sense, DF are the number of observations in a sample that are free to vary while estimating statistical parameters. You can also think of it as the amount of independent data that you can use to estimate a parameter.

Degrees of Freedom and Probability Distributions

Degrees of freedom also define the probability distributions for the test statistics of various hypothesis tests. For example, hypothesis tests use the t-distribution, F-distribution, and the chi-square distribution to determine statistical significance. Each of these probability distributions is a family of distributions where the degrees of freedom define the shape. Hypothesis tests use these distributions to calculate p-values. So, the degrees of freedom directly link to p-values through these distributions!

Next, let's look at how these distributions work for several hypothesis tests.

t-Distribution

T-tests are hypothesis tests for the mean and use the t-distribution to determine statistical significance.

A 1-sample t-test determines whether the difference between the sample mean and the null hypothesis value is statistically significant. Let's go back to our example of the mean. We know that when you have a sample and estimate the mean, you have n − 1 degrees of freedom, where n is the sample size. Consequently, for a 1-sample t-test, the degrees of freedom equals n − 1.

The degrees of freedom define the shape of the t-distribution that your t-test uses to calculate the p-value. The graph shows t-distributions for several different degrees of freedom. Because the degrees of freedom are so closely related to sample size, you can see the effect of sample size. As the degrees of freedom decreases, the t-distribution has thicker tails. This property allows for the greater uncertainty associated with small sample sizes.

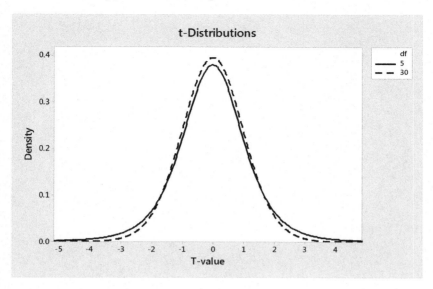

F-Distribution

The F-test in ANOVA also tests group means but for when you have at least three groups. It uses the F-distribution, which is defined by the degrees of freedom. However, you calculate the degrees of freedom for an F-distribution differently because an F-value is a ratio of two variances. Consequently, you have degrees of freedom for the numerator and denominator.

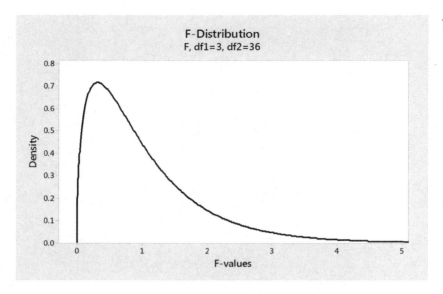

We'll cover the F-distribution when we talk about ANOVA in chapter 9.

Chi-Square Test of Independence

The chi-square test of independence determines whether there is a statistically significant relationship between categorical variables. Just like other hypothesis tests, this test incorporates degrees of freedom. For a table with r rows and c columns, the general rule for calculating degrees of freedom for a chi-square test is (r-1) (c-1).

However, we can create tables to understand it more intuitively. The degrees of freedom for a chi-square test of independence is the number of cells in the table that can vary before you can calculate all the other cells. In a chi-square table, the cells represent the observed frequency for each combination of categorical variables. The constraints are the totals in the margins.

Chi-Square 2 X 2 Table

For example, in a 2 X 2 table, after you enter one value in the table, you can calculate the remaining cells.

	Category A		Total
Category B	**15**	(4)	19
	(10)	(3)	13
Total	25	7	32

In the table, I entered the bold 15, and then I can calculate the remaining three values in parentheses. Therefore, this table has 1 DF.

Chi-Square 3 X 2 Table

Now, let's try a 3 X 2 table. The table below illustrates the example that I use in chapter 13 about the chi-square test of independence. In that section, I determine whether there is a statistically significant relationship between uniform color and deaths on the original *Star Trek* TV series.

	Shirt Color			Total
Status	**129**	**46**	(215)	390
	(7)	(9)	(24)	40
Total	136	55	239	430

In the table, one categorical variable is shirt color, which can be blue, gold, or red. The other categorical variable is status, which can be dead or alive. After I entered the two bolded values, I can calculate all the remaining cells. Consequently, this table has 2 DF.

We'll come back to this test in the section about the chi-square test of independence to show how it works and interpret the results using the *Star Trek* example.

Like the t-distribution and F-distribution, the chi-square distribution is a family of distributions where the degrees of freedom define the shape. Chi-square tests use this distribution to calculate p-values. The graph below displays several chi-square distributions.

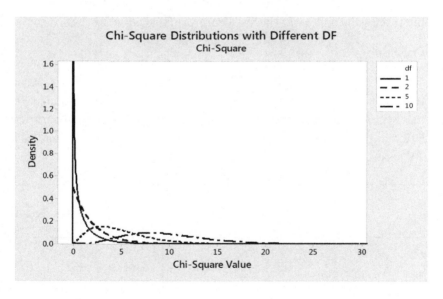

We'll cover chi-square tests in chapters 12 and 13. They're useful in a variety of contexts.

Degrees of Freedom in Regression Analysis

Degrees of freedom in regression is a bit more complicated, and I'll keep it on the simple side. In a regression model, each term is an estimated parameter that uses one degree of freedom. In the regression output, you can see how each term requires a DF. There are 28 observations and the two independent variables use a total of two degrees of freedom. The output displays the remaining 26 degrees of freedom in Error.

Regression Analysis: Temperature versus Pressure, Fuel Rate

Analysis of Variance

Source	DF	Adj SS	Adj MS	F-Value	P-Value
Regression	2	12608	6303.8	79.01	0.000
Pressure	1	2029	2028.9	25.43	0.000
Fuel Rate	1	12423	12423.1	155.71	0.000
Error	26	2074	79.8		
Total	28	14682			

The error degrees of freedom are the independent pieces of information that are available for estimating your coefficients. For precise coefficient estimates and powerful hypothesis tests in regression, you must have many error degrees of freedom, which equates to having many observations for each model term.

As you add terms to the model, the error degrees of freedom decreases. You have fewer pieces of information available to estimate the coefficients. This situation reduces the precision of the estimates and the power of the tests. When you have too few remaining degrees of freedom, you can't trust the regression results. If you use all your degrees of freedom, the procedure can't calculate the p-values.

Even though they might seem murky, degrees of freedom are essential to any statistical analysis! In a nutshell, degrees of freedom define the amount of information you have relative to the number of properties that you want to estimate. If you don't have enough data for what you want to do, you'll have imprecise estimates and low statistical power.

Central Limit Theorem

The central limit theorem is a crucial concept in statistics that affects hypothesis testing. This theorem states that, given a sufficiently large sample size, the sampling distribution of the mean for a variable will approximate a normal distribution regardless of that variable's distribution in the population.

Unpacking the meaning from that complex definition can be difficult. That's the topic for this section! I'll walk you through the various aspects of the central limit theorem (CLT) definition and show you why it is vital in statistics.

Distribution of the Variable in the Population

Part of the definition for the central limit theorem relates to "the variable's distribution in the population." This part is easy! In a population, the values of a variable can follow different probability distributions. These distributions can range from normal, left-skewed, right-skewed, and uniform among others.

Normal

Right-Skewed

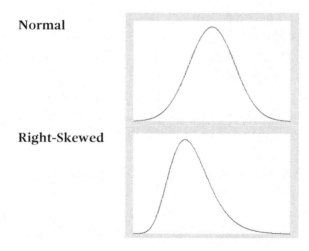

Left-Skewed

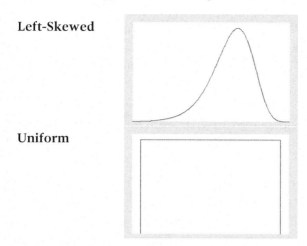

Uniform

This part of the definition refers to the distribution of the variable's values in the population from which you draw a random sample.

The central limit theorem applies to almost all types of probability distributions, but there are exceptions. For example, the population must have a finite variance. That restriction rules out the Cauchy distribution because it has infinite variance.

Additionally, the central limit theorem applies to independent, identically distributed variables. In other words, the value of one observation does not depend on the value of another observation. And, the distribution of that variable must remain constant across all measurements.

Sampling Distribution of the Mean

The definition for the central limit theorem also refers to "the sampling distribution of the mean." What's that? Hopefully, you remember this concept from chapter 1!

Typically, you perform a study once, and you might calculate the mean of that one sample. Now, imagine that you repeat the study many times and collect the same sample size for each one. Then, you calculate the mean for each of these samples and graph them on a histogram. The histogram displays the distribution of sample means, which statisticians refer to as the sampling distribution of the mean.

Fortunately, we don't have to repeat studies many times to estimate the sampling distribution of the mean. Statistical procedures can estimate that from a single random sample.

The shape of the sampling distribution depends on the sample size. If you perform the study using the same procedure and change only the sample size, the shape of the sampling distribution will differ for each sample size. And, that brings us to the next part of the CLT definition!

Sufficiently Large Sample Size

As the previous section states, the shape of the sampling distribution changes with the sample size. And, the definition of the central limit theorem states that when you have a sufficiently large sample size, the sampling distribution starts to approximate a normal distribution. How large does the sample size have to be for that approximation to occur?

It depends on the shape of the variable's distribution in the underlying population. The more the population distribution differs from being normal, the larger the sample size must be. Typically, statisticians say that a sample size of 30 is sufficient for most distributions. However, strongly skewed distributions can require larger sample sizes. We'll see the sample size aspect in action during the following empirical demonstration.

Approximating the Normal Distribution

The central limit theorem links the following two distributions:

- The distribution of the variable in the population.
- The sampling distribution of the mean.

Specifically, the CLT states that regardless of the variable's distribution in the population, the sampling distribution of the mean will tend to approximate the normal distribution. In other words, the population distribution can look like the following:

But the sampling distribution can appear like this:

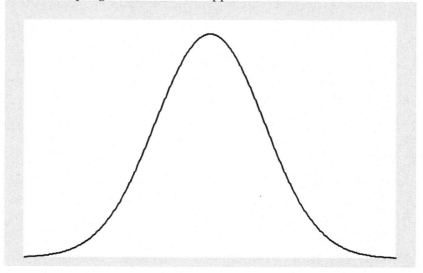

It's not surprising that a normally distributed variable produces a sampling distribution that also follows the normal distribution. But, surprisingly, nonnormal population distributions can also create normal sampling distributions.

Properties of the Central Limit Theorem

Let's get more specific about the normality features of the central limit theorem. Normal distributions have two parameters, the mean and standard deviation. What values do these parameters converge on?

As the sample size increases, the sampling distribution converges on a normal distribution where the mean equals the population mean, and the standard deviation equals $\sigma/\sqrt{n}$. Where:

- σ = the population standard deviation
- n = the sample size

As the sample size (n) increases, the standard deviation of the sampling distribution becomes smaller because the square root of the sample size is in the denominator. In other words, the sampling distribution clusters more tightly around the mean as sample size increases.

Let's put all of this together. As sample size increases, the sampling distribution more closely approximates the normal distribution, and the spread of that distribution tightens. These properties have essential implications in statistics that I'll discuss later in this section.

Empirical Demonstration

Now the fun part! There is a mathematical proof for the central theorem, but that goes beyond the scope of this introductory book. However, I will show how it works empirically by using statistical simulation software. I'll define population distributions and have the software draw many thousands of random samples from it. The software will calculate the mean of each sample and then graph these sample means on a histogram to display the sampling distribution of the mean.

For the following examples, I'll vary the sample size to show how that affects the sampling distribution. To produce the sampling distribution, I'll draw 500,000 random samples because that creates a smooth distribution in the histogram.

Keep this critical difference in mind. While I'll collect a consistent 500,000 samples per condition, the size of those samples will vary, and that affects the shape of the sampling distribution.

Let's test this theory! To do that, I'll use Statistics101, which is a giftware computer program.

Testing the CLT with Three Probability Distributions

I'll show you how the central limit theorem works with three different distributions: moderately skewed, severely skewed, and a uniform distribution. The first two distributions skew to the right and follow the lognormal distribution. The probability distribution plot displays the distribution of values in two populations. Notice how the dashed distribution is much more severely skewed. It actually extends quite a way off the graph! We'll see how this makes a difference in the sampling distributions.

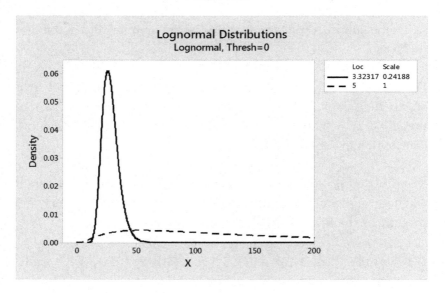

Let's see how the central limit theorem handles these two distributions and the uniform distribution.

Moderately Skewed Distribution

The following graph shows the moderately skewed lognormal distribution. This distribution fits the body fat percentage dataset that I use in in chapter 10 for identifying the distribution of continuous data. I use the simulation software to draw random samples from this population 500,000 times for each sample size (5, 20, 40).

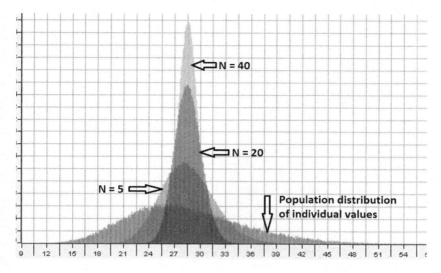

In the graph above, the broadest distribution represents the skewed distribution of individual values in the population. The other distributions represent the sampling distributions of the means for different sample sizes. The distribution for a sample size of 5 is still skewed because each sample is so small. However, the sampling distributions for the larger sample sizes of 20 and 40 are not visibly skewed. They are approximately normal. The N = 40 distribution has the tightest range, which indicates that sample means are unlikely to fall far from the population mean.

As the sample size increases, the sampling distributions more closely approximate the normal distribution and become more tightly clustered around the population mean—just as the central limit theorem states!

Very Skewed Distribution

Now, let's try this with the very skewed lognormal distribution. I follow the same process but use larger sample sizes of 40, 60, and 80. I do not include the population distribution in this one because it is so skewed that it messes up the X-axis scale!

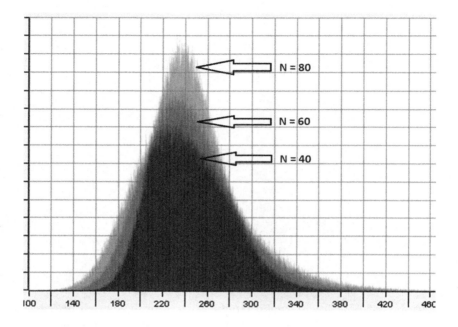

The population distribution is extremely skewed. It's probably more skewed than real data tend to be. As you can see, even with the largest sample size (N =80), the sampling distribution of the mean is still skewed right. However, it is less skewed than the sampling distributions for the smaller sample sizes. Also, notice how the peaks of the sampling distribution shift to the right as the sample increases.

Eventually, with a large enough sample size, the sampling distributions will become symmetric, and the peak will stop shifting and center on the actual population mean. Given the lognormal parameters, I can calculate that the population mean is 244.7. The peak of the N = 80 curve is near 240, so it is closing in on the correct value.

If your population distribution is extremely skewed, be aware that you might need a substantial sample size for the central limit theorem to kick in and produce sampling distributions that approximate a normal distribution! However, please note that the extremely skewed example is severe enough to surpass the skew present in most real datasets.

Uniform Distribution

Now, let's change gears and look at an entirely different type of distribution. Imagine that we roll a die and take the average value of the rolls. The probabilities for rolling the numbers on a die follow a uniform distribution because all numbers have the same chance of occurring. Can the central limit theorem work with discrete numbers and uniform probabilities? Let's see!

In the graph below, I use the same procedure as before. In this example, the sample size refers to the number of times we roll the die. The process calculates the mean for each sample.

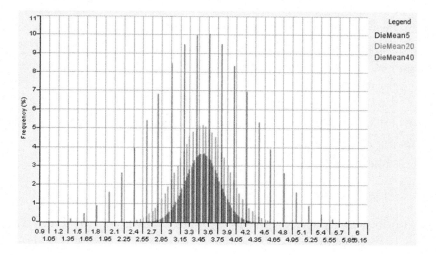

In the chart, I use sample sizes of 5, 20, and 40. We'd expect the average to be $(1 + 2 + 3 + 4 + 5 + 6 / 6 = 3.5)$. All the sampling distributions center on this value. As we increase the sample size, the sampling distributions more closely approximate a normal distribution and have a tighter range. Just as the central limit theorem predicts!

You could perform a similar experiment using the binomial distribution with coin flips and obtain the same types of results when it comes to, say, the probability of getting heads. All thanks to the central limit theorem!

Why is the Central Limit Theorem Important?

The central limit theorem is vital in hypothesis testing for two main reasons—the normality assumption and the precision of the estimates.

Central limit theorem and the normality assumption

The fact that sampling distributions can approximate a normal distribution has critical implications. In statistics, the normality assumption is vital for parametric hypothesis tests of the mean, such as the t-test. Consequently, you might think that these tests are not valid when the data are nonnormally distributed.

However, if your sample size is large enough, the central limit theorem kicks in and produces sampling distributions that approximate a normal distribution. This fact allows you to use these hypothesis tests even when your data are nonnormally distributed—if your sample size is large enough.

Recall that t-tests are robust to departures from the normality assumption when your sample size is sufficiently large. That's thanks to the central limit theorem!

Precision of estimates

In all the graphs, notice how the sampling distributions of the mean cluster more tightly around the population mean as the sample sizes increase. This property of the central limit theorem becomes relevant when using a sample to estimate the mean of an entire population. With a larger sample size, your sample mean is more likely to be close to the real population mean. In other words, your estimate is more precise.

Conversely, the sampling distributions of the mean for smaller sample sizes are much broader. For small sample sizes, it's not unusual for sample means to be further away from the actual population mean. You obtain less precise estimates.

In closing, understanding the central limit theorem is crucial when it comes to trusting the validity of your results and assessing the precision of your estimates. Use large sample sizes to satisfy the normality assumption even when your data are nonnormally distributed and to obtain more precise estimates!

Review and Next Steps

In this chapter, we saw why large sample sizes are a good thing from two different angles, degrees of freedom and the central limit theorem.

Degrees of freedom relate to the amount of independent information available to estimate the parameters for our hypothesis tests. Having more information per parameter produces more precise estimates and more powerful tests.

Then, we used the central limit theorem to consider sample size. We found that larger samples allow us to waive the normality assumption, and they produce more precise estimates for the populations that we're studying.

Large samples are great for a variety of reasons!

From here on out, the book looks at the vast array of hypothesis tests you can perform on various types of data. We started by focusing on using t-tests to compares means. You got your feet wet on this test and learned about all the related concepts: assumptions, sample estimates versus population parameters, test statistics, sampling distributions, critical regions, error rates, p-values, and significance levels.

Now you're ready to apply these concepts to other tests because the underlying mechanics are similar.

CHAPTER 8

Data Types and
Hypothesis Tests

Throughout this book, we've focused on using t-tests with continuous data to assess means. In this chapter, we'll look at various data types and how you can analyze them. For now, my goal is to show you the spectrum of what's possible in terms of data types and hypothesis tests. Later chapters present detailed information about the hypothesis tests themselves.

You will learn about common hypothesis tests for continuous, binary, count, categorical, and ordinal data. Understanding the various data types is crucial because they determine the hypothesis tests you can perform and, critically, the nature of the conclusions that you can draw. If you collect the wrong data, you might not be able to get the answers you need.

I'll define each of these data types, the characteristics you can learn from them, and the standard hypothesis tests you can use. Each test I cover has a link that takes you to the detailed section about that test in a later chapter.

Continuous Data

I've already defined continuous data in this book. But I'll do so again so it's easy to compare to the other data types. The t-tests we've been looking at require continuous data, but there are other tests you can perform on continuous data.

Continuous data can take on any numeric value, and it can be meaningfully divided into smaller increments, including fractional and decimal values. There is an infinite number of possible values between any two values. You often measure a continuous variable on a scale. For example, when you measure height, weight, and temperature, you have continuous data.

With continuous variables, you can use hypothesis tests to assess the mean, median, standard deviation, distribution, and correlations of the data.

When you collect continuous data, you usually get more bang for your data buck than for discrete data. The two key advantages of continuous data are that you can:

- Draw conclusions with a smaller sample size.
- Use a wider variety of analyses, which allows you to learn more.

Suppose we have two production methods and our goal is to determine which one produces a stronger product. To evaluate the two methods, we draw a random sample of 30 products from each production line and measure each unit's strength. Before performing any analyses, it's always smart to graph the data because it provides an excellent overview. Use this CSV data file to follow along: Continuous_Data_Examples.

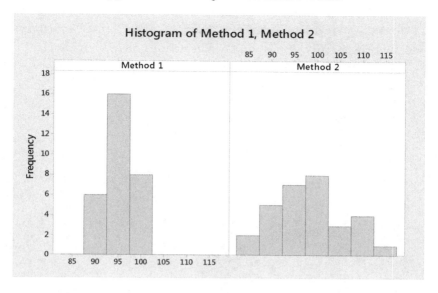

Hypothesis tests for continuous data can assess both the central tendency and variability. These histograms suggest that Method 2 produces a higher mean strength, while Method 1 produces more consistent strength scores. The higher mean strength is good for our product, but the greater variability might produce more defects.

When you're testing a measure of central tendency, it's usually the mean. However, there is also a class of tests that assess the median rather than the mean. These are known as nonparametric tests and practitioners use them less frequently. However, consider using a nonparametric test if your data are highly skewed and the median better represents the actual center of your data than the mean. This book doesn't focus on nonparametric tests, but it does provide a general overview.

When you have two continuous variables, you can graph them using a scatterplot. Scatterplots are great for displaying the relationship between two continuous variables. The scatterplot shows how height and weight tend to increase together. Correlation describes the strength of this relationship numerically using values that range from

-1 to +1. Correlation includes a hypothesis test that determines whether the relationship is statistically significant.

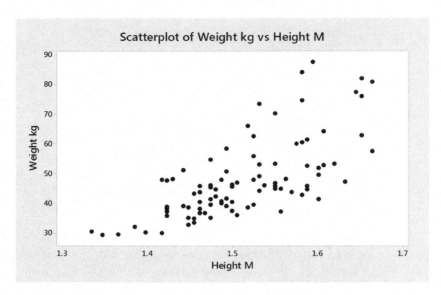

We can also use hypothesis tests to assess the shape of the distribution. For example, the data below don't appear to fit the normal distribution, but what distribution does it follow?

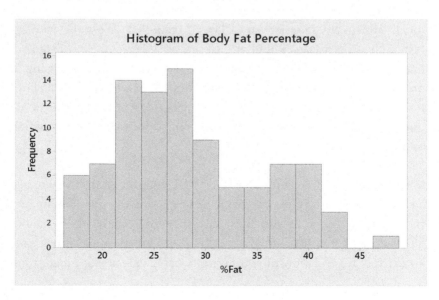

Keep these graphs of continuous data in mind when we look at binary data because they illustrate how continuous data convey much more information than other types.

The table below summarizes hypothesis tests that are available for continuous data. Note that categorical variables define the comparison groups.

What you're testing	Hypothesis Test
One mean to reference value	1-sample t-test (p36)
Means for two groups	2-sample t-test (p40), Paired t (p45), Comparing CIs (p53)
Means for at least three groups	One-Way ANOVA (p193), Two-Way ANOVA (p220)
Compare specific groups from ANOVA	Post hoc tests (p205), Tukey's Method (p211), Dunnett's Method (p216), Hsu's MCB (p217)
One standard deviation to reference	1 Sample Variance Test (p233)
Standard deviations for two groups	2 Sample Variance Test (p236)
Correlation between two continuous variables	Pearson's correlation coefficient (p239)
Shape of distribution	Distribution tests for continuous data (p242)
Presences of outliers	Outlier test (p268)
Medians	Nonparametric tests (p332), Mann-Whitney Test (p340)

Binary Data

Binary data can have only two values. If you can place an observation into only two categories, you have a binary variable. Statisticians also refer to binary data as both dichotomous data and indicator variables. For example, pass/fail, male/female, and the presence/absence of a characteristic are all binary data. Quality improvement practitioners often use binary data to record defective units.

Binary data are useful for calculating proportions or percentages, such as the proportion of defective products in a sample. You simply take the number of defective products and divide by the sample size. Hypothesis tests that assess proportions require binary data and allow you to use sample data to make inferences about the proportions of populations.

Suppose we take a random sample of our product from two production lines. Inspectors evaluate each product and either accept or reject it. We can use hypothesis tests to compare the proportion of defects between samples.

The table below summarizes hypothesis tests that are available for binary data. Note that categorical variables define the comparison groups.

What you're testing	Hypothesis Test
One proportion to a target.	1 Proportions Test (p275)
Proportions for two groups.	2 Proportions Test (p278)

Comparing Continuous Data to Binary Data

Think back to the graphs for the continuous data. At a glance, you can see both the central location and spread of the data. If we added spec limits, we could see how many data points are close and far away from them. Is the process centered between the spec limits? Continuous data provide a lot of insight into our processes.

Now, compare that to the binary data where we just learn the proportion of defects. There is no distribution to analyze, no indication of how close the items are to the specs, and no hint of how they failed the inspection.

Additionally, proportions tests for binary data require larger samples than tests for continuous data. When the difference between proportions is smaller, the required sample sizes can become quite large.
In general, binary data provide less information than an equivalent amount of continuous data. If you can collect continuous data, it's the better route to take!

Count Data

Count data can have only non-negative integers (e.g., 0, 1, 2, etc.). In statistics, we often model count data using the Poisson distribution. Poisson data are a count of the presence of a characteristic, result, or activity over a constant amount of time, area, or other length of observation. For example, you can use count data to record the number of defects per item or defective units per batch. With Poisson data, you can assess the rate of occurrence.

Imagine that we receive shipments of parts from two different suppliers. Each supplier sends the parts in the same sized batch. Inspectors count the number of defective items per batch. We need to determine whether one supplier produces fewer defects per batch than the other supplier.

The table below summarizes hypothesis tests that are available for count data. Note that categorical variables define the comparison groups.

What you're testing	Hypothesis Test
One rate to a target.	1 Sample Poisson Rate Test (p301)
Rates for two groups.	2 Sample Poisson Rate Test (p303)
Do your counts following the Poisson distribution?	Poisson Goodness-of-Fit Test (p306)

Categorical Data

Categorical data have values that you can put into a countable number of distinct groups based on a characteristic. For a categorical variable, you can assign categories, but the categories have no natural order. Analysts also refer to categorical data as both attribute and nominal variables.

For example, college major is a categorical variable with values such as psychology, political science, engineering, biology, etc.

Categorical variables can define groups in your data that you want to compare. For example, if you're using one-way ANOVA to compare the mean salaries by college major. College major is the categorical grouping variable, while salary is the continuous outcome, or dependent, variable. Categorical variables can also define the groups in 2-sample tests, such as the treatment and control groups.

Categorical variables have a distribution of values that you can assess as proportions of the whole.

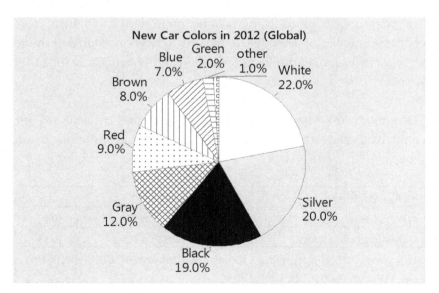

Just as there is a correlation between two continuous variables, two categorical variables can have an association. If you know one characteristic of an item or person, does that knowledge help you predict the value of another aspect of the same item/person?

For example, is there an association between:

- Educational level and marital status?
- Political party affiliation and religious affiliation?
- Gender and ice cream flavor preference?
- Uniform color in Star Trek and survival status?

Two-way contingency tables often represent the frequency of combinations for two categorical variables. These tables help identify relationships between a pair of categorical variables. Each value in a table cell indicates the number of times researchers observed a particular combination of categorical values.

In the table below, the two categorical variables are gender and ice cream flavor preference. Each cell represents the number of times members of one gender preferred a particular ice cream flavor.

Gender	Chocolate	Strawberry	Vanilla	Total
Female	37	17	12	66
Male	21	18	32	71
Total	58	35	44	137

The following table summarizes hypothesis tests that are available for categorical data.

What you're testing	Hypothesis Test
Association between two categorical variables.	Chi-Squared Test of Independence (p311)
Do the proportions of values follow a hypothesized distribution?	Chi-Square Goodness-of-Fit test (p326)

Ordinal Data

Ordinal data have at least three categories and they have a natural order. Examples of ordinal variables include overall status (poor to excellent), agreement (strongly disagree to strongly agree), and rank (such as sporting teams).

Ordinal variables have a combination of qualitative and quantitative properties. On the one hand, these variables have a limited number of discrete values like categorical variables. On the other hand, the differences between the values provide some information like quantitative variables. However, the difference between adjacent values might not be consistent. For example, first, second, and third in a race are ordinal data. However, the difference in time between first and second place might not be the same as the difference between second and third place.

Analysts often represent ordinal variables using numbers, such as a 1-5 Likert scale that measures satisfaction. In number form, you can calculate average scores as with quantitative variables. However, the numbers have limited usefulness because the differences between ranks might not be constant.

Analyzing ordinal data is tricky because of the mix of qualitative and quantitative properties. Tests for continuous data and categorical data aren't quite right. If you're working with ranks, you're in luck because many nonparametric tests analyze that type. However, there is a debate over how to handle Likert scale data. The chapter about nonparametric tests discusses these issues.

Review and Next Steps

In broad strokes, we covered the different types of data, what you can learn from each type, and the hypothesis tests you can use. Now, let's dive in and take an up-close look at these hypothesis tests!

CHAPTER 9

ANOVA Compares More Than Two Groups

In this chapter, we'll continue with continuous data and comparing group means. We covered t-tests in depth throughout the first half of this book—so I won't revisit them here. However, if you'll recall, you can use t-tests to compare the means of two groups at most. What do you do if you have three groups or more? Use analysis of variance (ANOVA)!

One-Way ANOVA

Use one-way ANOVA to determine whether the means of at least three groups are different.

One-way ANOVA is a hypothesis test that allows you to compare more group means. Like all hypothesis tests, one-way ANOVA uses sample data to make inferences about the properties of an entire population.

One-way Analysis of Variance (ANOVA) requires one categorical factor for the independent variable and a continuous variable for the dependent variable. The values of the categorical factor divide the continuous data into groups. The test determines whether the mean differences between these groups are statistically significant. For example, if fertilizer type is your categorical variable, you can assess whether the differences between plant growth means for at least three fertilizers are statistically significant.

Technically, you can use one-way ANOVA to compare two groups. However, if you have two groups, you'll typically use a two-sample t-test.

The standard hypotheses for one-way ANOVA are the following:

- Null: All group means are equal.
- Alternative: Not all group means are equal.

If the p-value is less than your significance level (usually 0.05), reject the null hypothesis. Your sample data support the hypothesis that the mean of at least one population is different from the other population means.

Assumptions

For reliable One-Way ANOVA results, your data should satisfy the following assumptions:

- Random samples
- Independent groups

The dependent variable is continuous

The dependent variable is the outcome you are measuring. The procedure compares the group means of this variable. For example, salary is a continuous variable, and you can compare mean salaries by groups.

The independent variable is categorical

The levels of the categorical variable define the groups that you are comparing. For example, college major is a categorical variable. Categorical variables in ANOVA are also known as factors.

Your sample data should follow a normal distribution or each group has more than 15 or 20 observations

ANOVA procedures assume that your data follow the normal distribution. However, as you saw for t-tests, you can waive this assumption if your sample size is large enough.

For one-way ANOVA, when you have 2-9 groups and each group is larger than 15, your data can be skewed and the test results will still be reliable. When you have 10-12 groups, you should have at least 20 per group to waive the normality assumption.

If your data are non-normal and your sample sizes are smaller than these guidelines, the test results can be unreliable.

Groups should have roughly equal variances or use Welch's ANOVA

The standard F-test form of One-Way ANOVA assumes that the variance within each of the populations is equal. Variance is a measure of variability and equals the standard deviation squared. The standard guideline is that you can assume the population variances are equal if no group in your sample has twice the variance of another group.

However, if you are not confident that the variances are equal, use Welch's ANOVA, which does not assume equal variances.

Example One-Way ANOVA

Let's conduct a one-way ANOVA! Our example scenario is that we are comparing the strength of raw material from four suppliers. Supplier is our categorical independent variable (factor), while strength is the continuous dependent variable. We draw a random sample of 10 units of material from each supplier and measure each unit's strength. Next, we want to determine whether the mean strengths of the material from the four suppliers are different.

For our example, each column represents raw material from one supplier. Use this CSV data file: OneWayExample.

Strength 1	Strength 2	Strength 3	Strength 4
11.715501	10.566155	10.283346	6.903486
11.981569	13.455359	12.177732	8.9901103
8.0439292	7.4188405	10.559808	6.9712734
10.55816	12.031314	9.6551865	9.1603896
14.079463	7.7766332	8.7902748	8.6784264
10.776867	10.748939	10.862457	11.443832
7.8602695	10.72698	10.378184	10.780441
11.889672	4.4772914	10.188052	5.66676
11.942314	6.8038204	11.62452	10.776041
13.177454	5.3718922	12.305905	9.0087649

```
Analysis of Variance

Source   DF   Adj SS   Adj MS   F-Value  P-Value
Factor    3    43.62   14.540      3.30    0.031
Error    36   158.47    4.402
Total    39   202.09


Model Summary

        S     R-sq   R-sq(adj)   R-sq(pred)
  2.09805   21.58%      15.05%         3.19%

Means

Factor    N     Mean    StDev        95% CI
1        10   11.203    1.995  (9.857, 12.548)
2        10    8.938    2.980  (7.592, 10.283)
3        10   10.683    1.102  (9.337, 12.028)
4        10    8.838    1.879  (7.492, 10.184)
```

Interpreting the One-Way ANOVA Results

The Means table indicates that the mean strengths range from a low of 8.838 for supplier 4 to a high of 11.203 for supplier 1. Our sample means are different. However, we need to determine whether our data support the notion that the population means are not equal. The differences we see in our samples might be the result of random sampling error.

In the ANOVA table, the p-value is 0.031. Because this value is less than our significance level of 0.05, we reject the null hypothesis. Our sample data provide sufficient evidence to conclude that the four population means are not equal.

Note in the Analysis of Variance table that One-Way ANOVA uses the F-value for its test statistic. Next, we'll continue to use this example to delve into how the F-test assesses means.

How F-tests work in ANOVA

Analysis of variance (ANOVA) uses F-tests to statistically assess the equality of means when you have three or more groups. In this section, I'll answer several common questions about the F-test.

- How do F-tests work?
- Why do we analyze *variances* to test *means*?

I'll use concepts and graphs to answer these questions about F-tests using the previous one-way ANOVA example.

It's an F-test because these tests use the F-statistic to test the hypotheses. An F-statistic is the ratio of two variances, and it was named after Sir Ronald Fisher. Variances measure the dispersal of the data points around the mean. Higher variances occur when the individual data points tend to fall further from the mean.

It's challenging to interpret variances directly because they are in squared units of the data. If you take the square root of the variance, you obtain the standard deviation, which is easier to interpret because it uses the data units. While variances are hard to interpret directly, some statistical tests use them in their calculations.

An F-statistic is the ratio of two variances, or technically, two mean squares. Mean squares are variances that account for the degrees of freedom (DF) used to estimate the variance.

Think of it this way. Variances are the sum of the squared deviations from the mean. If you have a bigger sample, there are more squared deviations to add up. The result is that the sum becomes larger and larger as you add in more observations. By incorporating the degrees of freedom, mean squares account for the differing numbers of measurements for each variance estimate. Otherwise, the variances are not comparable, and the ratio for the F-statistic is meaningless.

Given that F-tests evaluate the ratio of two variances, you might think it's only suitable for determining whether the variances are equal. Actually, it can do that and a lot more! F-tests are surprisingly flexible because you can include different variances in the ratio to test a wide variety of properties. F-tests can compare the fits of different models, assess the overall significance in regression models, test specific terms in linear models, and determine whether a set of means are all equal.

The F-test in One-Way ANOVA

We want to determine whether a set of means are all equal. To evaluate this condition with an F-test, we need to use the proper variances in the ratio. Here's the F-statistic ratio for one-way ANOVA.

$$F = \frac{\text{Between Groups Variance}}{\text{Within Group Variance}}$$

To see how F-tests work, I'll go through the one-way ANOVA example from the previous section. I'll reference the numeric results from that example as I illustrate how the test works.

F-test Numerator: Between-Groups Variance

The one-way ANOVA procedure calculates the average for each of the four groups in the example: 11.203, 8.938, 10.683, and 8.838. The means of these groups spread out around the global mean (9.915) for all 40 data points. The further the groups are from the global mean, the larger the variance in the numerator becomes.

It's easier to say that the group means are different when they are further apart. That's self-evident, right? In our F-test, this corresponds to having a higher variance in the numerator.

The dot plot illustrates how this works by comparing two sets of group means. This graph represents each group's mean with a dot. The between-group variance increases as the dots spread out.

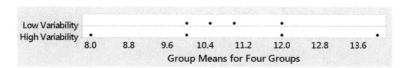

Looking back at the one-way ANOVA output, which statistic do we use for the between-group variance? The value we use is the adjusted mean square for Factor (Adj MS 15.540). The interpretation of this number is not intuitive because it is the sum of the squared distances from the global mean divided by the factor DF. The relevant point is that this number increases as the group means spread further apart.

F-test Denominator: Within-Groups Variance

Now we move on to the F-test denominator, which factors in the variances within each group. This variance measures the distance between each data point and its group mean. Again, it is the sum of the squared distances divided by the error DF.

This variance is small when the data points within each group are closer to their group mean. As the data points within each group spread out further from their group mean, the within-group variance increases.

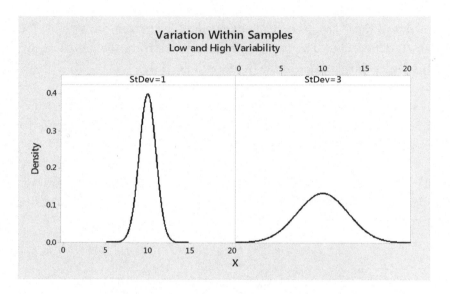

The graph compares low within-group variability to high within-group variability. The distributions represent how tightly the data points within each group cluster around the group mean. The F-statistic denominator, or the within-group variance, is higher for the right panel because the data points tend to be further from the group average.

To conclude that the group means are not equal, you want low within-group variance. Why? The within-group variance represents the variation that the model does not explain. Statisticians refer to this as random error. As the error increases, it becomes more likely that the observed differences between group means are caused by the error rather than by actual differences at the population level. Obviously, you want low amounts of error!

Let's refer to the ANOVA output again. The within-group variance appears in the output as the adjusted mean squares for error (Adj MS for Error): 4.402.

The F-Statistic: Ratio of Between-Groups to Within-Groups Variances

F-statistics are the ratio of two variances that are approximately equal when the null hypothesis is true, which yields F-statistics near 1.

We looked at the two different variances used in a one-way ANOVA F-test. Now, let's put them together to see which combinations produce low and high F-statistics. In the graphs, notice how the spread of the group means (lines) compares to the data point spread within each group (curves).

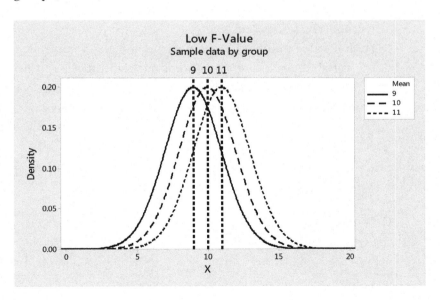

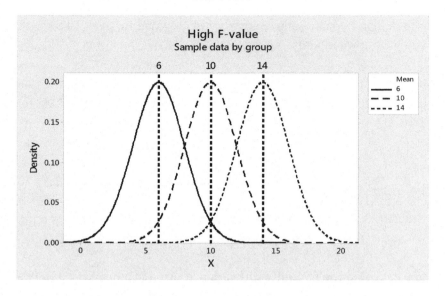

- **Low F-value graph**: The group means cluster together more tightly than the within-group variability. The distance between the means is small relative to the random error within each group. You can't conclude that these groups are truly different at the population level.
- **High F-value graph**: The group means spread out more than the variability of the data within groups. In this case, it becomes more likely that the observed differences between group means reflect differences at the population level.

How to Calculate our F-value

Going back to our example output, we can use our F-ratio numerator and denominator to calculate our F-value like this:

$$F = \frac{\text{Between Groups Variance}}{\text{Within Group Variance}} = \frac{14.540}{4.402} = 3.30$$

To conclude that not all group means are equal, we need a large F-value to reject the null hypothesis. Is ours large enough?

A tricky thing about F-values is that they are a unitless statistic, which makes them hard to interpret. Our F-value of 3.30 indicates that the between-groups variance is 3.3 times the size of the within-group variance. The null hypothesis value is that variances are equal, which produces an F-value of 1. Is our F-value of 3.3 large enough to reject the null hypothesis?

We don't know precisely how uncommon our F-value is if the null hypothesis is correct. To interpret individual F-values, we need to place them in a larger context. F-distributions provide this broader context and allow us to calculate probabilities.

How F-tests Use F-distributions to Test Hypotheses

A single F-test produces a single F-value. However, imagine we perform the following process.

First, let's assume that the null hypothesis is correct for the population. At the population level, all four group means are equal. Now, we repeat our study many times by drawing many random samples from this population using the same one-way ANOVA design (four groups with 10 samples per group). Next, we perform one-way ANOVA on all the samples and plot the distribution of the F-values.

If we follow this procedure, we produce a graph that displays the distribution of F-values for a population where the null hypothesis is true. As you will recall from t-tests, we use sampling distributions to calculate probabilities for how unlikely our sample statistic is if the null hypothesis is correct. F-tests use the F-distribution.

Fortunately, we don't need to collect numerous random samples to create this graph! Statisticians understand the properties of F-distributions, which allows us to estimate the sampling distribution using the F-distribution and the details of our one-way ANOVA design.

Our goal is to evaluate whether our sample F-value is so rare that it justifies rejecting the null hypothesis for the entire population. We'll calculate the probability of obtaining an F-value that is at least as high as our study's value (3.30).

This probability is the p-value! A low probability indicates that our sample data are unlikely when the null hypothesis is true.

Graphing the F-test for Our One-Way ANOVA Example

For one-way ANOVA, the degrees of freedom in the numerator and the denominator define the F-distribution for a design. There is a different F-distribution for each study design. I'll create a probability distribution plot based on the DF indicated in the statistical output example. Our study has 3 DF in the numerator and 36 in the denominator.

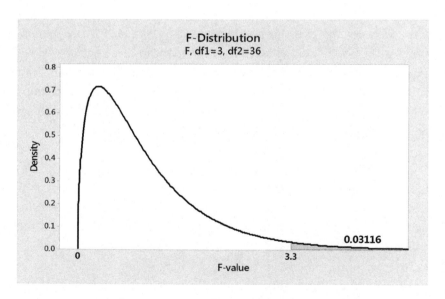

The distribution curve displays the likelihood of F-values for a population where the four group means are equal at the population level. I shaded the region that corresponds to F-values greater than or equal to our study's F-value (3.3). When the null hypothesis is true, F-values fall in this area approximately 3.1% of the time. Using a significance level of 0.05, our sample data are unusual enough to warrant rejecting the null hypothesis. The sample evidence suggests that not all group means are equal.

Why We Analyze Variances to Test Means

Let's return to the question about why we analyze variances to determine whether the group means are different. Focus on the "means are different" aspect. This part explicitly involves the variation of the group means. If there is no variation in the means, they can't be different, right? Similarly, the larger the differences between the means, the more variation must be present.

ANOVA and F-tests assess the amount of variability between the group means in the context of the variation within groups to determine whether the mean differences are statistically significant.

I'm sure you've noticed something. When you have a significant p-value and reject the null hypothesis, you know that not all the means are equal. Okay, that's nice. But what if you need to know specifically which pairs of means are significantly different? Let me introduce you to post hoc tests for ANOVA!

Using Post Hoc Tests with ANOVA

Post hoc tests are an integral part of ANOVA. When you use ANOVA to test the equality of at least three group means, statistically significant results indicate that not all the group means are equal. However, ANOVA results do not identify which particular differences between pairs of means are significant. Use post hoc tests to explore differences between multiple group means while controlling the experiment-wise error rate.

In this section, I'll show you what post hoc analyses are, the critical benefits they provide, and help you choose the correct one for your study. Additionally, I'll explain why failure to control the experiment-wise error rate will cause you to have severe doubts about your results.

Typically, when you want to determine whether three or more means are different, you'll perform ANOVA. Statisticians refer to the ANOVA F-test as an omnibus test.

An omnibus test provides overall results for your data. Collectively, are the differences between the means statistically significant—Yes or No?

If the p-value from your ANOVA F-test is less than your significance level, you can reject the null hypothesis.

- Null: All group means are equal.
- Alternative: Not all group means are equal.

However, ANOVA test results don't map out which groups are different from other groups. As you can see from these hypotheses, if you can reject the null, you only know that not all the means are equal. Sometimes you really need to know which groups are significantly different from other groups!

Example One-Way ANOVA to Use with Post Hoc Tests

We'll start with this one-way ANOVA example, and then use it to illustrate three post hoc tests. Imagine we are testing four materials that we're considering for making a product part. We want to determine whether the mean differences between the strengths of these four materials are statistically significant. We obtain the following one-way ANOVA results. To follow along with this example, use this CSV dataset: PostHocTests.

One-way ANOVA: Strength versus Material

Method

Null hypothesis   All means are equal
Alternative hypothesis   At least one mean is different
Significance level $\alpha = 0.05$

Equal variances were assumed for the analysis.

Factor Information

Factor   Levels Values
Material   4   A, B, C, D

Analysis of Variance

Source	DF	Adj SS	Adj MS	F-Value	P-Value
Material	3	281.7	93.90	6.02	0.004
Error	20	312.1	15.60		
Total	23	593.8			

Means

Factor	N	Mean	StDev	95% CI
1	6	37.73	3.36	(34.37, 41.10)
2	6	31.57	5.50	(28.20, 34.93)
3	6	35.98	3.73	(32.62, 39.35)
4	6	41.07	2.64	(37.70, 44.43)

The p-value of 0.004 indicates that we can reject the null hypothesis and conclude that the four means are not all equal. The Means table at the bottom displays the group means. However, we don't know which pairs of groups are significantly different.

To compare group means, we need to perform post hoc tests, also known as multiple comparisons. In Latin, post hoc means "after this." You conduct post hoc analyses after a statistically significant omnibus test.

Before we get to these group comparisons, you need to learn about the experiment-wise error rate.

What is the Experiment-wise Error Rate?

Post hoc tests perform two vital tasks. Yes, they tell you which group means are significantly different from other group means. Crucially, they also control the experiment-wise, or familywise, error rate. In this context, experiment-wise, family-wise, and family error rates are all synonyms that I'll use interchangeably.

What is this experiment-wise error rate? For every hypothesis test you perform, there is a type I error rate, which your significance level (alpha) defines. In other words, there's a chance that you'll reject a null hypothesis that is actually true—a false positive. When you perform only one test, the type I error rate equals your significance level, which is often 5%. However, as you conduct more and more tests, your chance of a false positive increases. If you perform enough tests, you're virtually guaranteed to get a false positive! The error rate for a family of tests is always higher than an individual test.

Imagine you're rolling a pair of dice and rolling two ones (known as snake eyes) represents a Type I error. The probability of snake eyes for a single roll is ~2.8% rather than 5%, but you get the idea. If you roll the dice just once, your chances of rolling snake eyes aren't too bad. However, the more times you roll the dice, the more likely you'll get two ones. With 25 rolls, snake eyes become more likely than not (50.8%). With enough rolls, it becomes inevitable.

Family Error Rates in ANOVA

In the ANOVA context, you want to compare the group means. The more groups you have, the more comparison tests you need to perform. For our example ANOVA with four groups (A B C D), we'll need to make the following six comparisons.

- A – B
- A – C
- A – D
- B – C
- B – D
- C – D

$4 \, C^3 \qquad \dfrac{4 \times 3}{2 \times 1} = 6$

Our experiment includes this family of six comparisons. Each comparison represents a roll of the dice for obtaining a false positive. What's the error rate for six comparisons? Unfortunately, as you'll see next, the experiment-wise error rate snowballs based on the number of groups in your experiment.

The next table shows how increasing the number of groups in your study causes the number of comparisons to rise, which in turn raises the family-wise error rate. Notice how quickly the quantity of comparisons increases by adding just a few groups! Correspondingly, the experiment-wise error rate rapidly becomes problematic.

The table starts with two groups, and the single comparison between them has an experiment-wise error rate that equals the significance level (0.05). Unfortunately, the family-wise error rate rapidly increases from there!

All Pairwise Comparisons Alpha = 0.05		
Groups	Comparisons	Experiment-wise Error Rate
2	1	0.05
3	3	0.142625
4	6	0.264908109
5	10	0.401263061
6	15	0.53670877
7	21	0.659438374
8	28	0.762173115
9	36	0.842220785
10	45	0.900559743
11	55	0.940461445
12	66	0.966134464
13	78	0.981700416
14	91	0.990606054
15	105	0.995418807

The formula for the maximum number of comparisons you can make for N groups is: $(N*(N-1))/2$. The total number of comparisons is the family of comparisons for your experiment when you compare all possible pairs of groups (i.e., all pairwise comparisons). Additionally, the formula for calculating the error rate for the entire set of comparisons is $1 - (1 - \alpha)^C$. Alpha is your significance level for a single comparison, and C equals the number of comparisons.

⟶ $(1-\alpha)^C$ is no false positive for C times.

The experiment-wise error rate represents the probability of a type I error (false positive) over the total family of comparisons. Our ANOVA example has four groups, which produces six comparisons and a family-wise error rate of 0.26. If you increase the groups to five, the error rate jumps to 40%! When you have 15 groups, you are virtually guaranteed to have a false positive (99.5%)!

Post Hoc Tests Control the Experiment-wise Error Rate

The table succinctly illustrates the problem that post hoc tests resolve. Typically, when performing statistical analysis, you expect a false positive rate of 5%, or whatever value you set for the significance level. As the table shows, when you increase the number of groups from 2 to 3, the error rate nearly triples from 0.05 to 0.143. And, it quickly worsens from there!

These error rates are too high! Upon seeing a significant difference between groups, you would have severe doubts about whether it was a false positive rather than a real difference.

If you use 2-sample t-tests to systematically compare all group means in your study, you'll encounter this problem. You'd set the significance level for each test (e.g., 0.05), and then the number of comparisons will determine the experiment-wise error rate, as shown in the table.

Fortunately, post hoc tests use a different approach. For these tests, you set the experiment-wise error rate you want for the entire set of comparisons. Then, the post hoc test calculates the significance level for all individual comparisons that produces the familywise error rate you specify.

Understanding how post hoc tests work is much simpler when you see them in action. Let's get back to our one-way ANOVA example!

Tukey's Method

For our ANOVA example, we have four groups that require six comparisons to cover all combinations of groups. We'll use a post hoc test and specify that the family of six comparisons should collectively produce a familywise error rate of 0.05. The post hoc test I'll use is Tukey's method. There are a variety of post hoc tests you can choose from, but Tukey's method is the most common for comparing all possible group pairings.

There are two ways to present post hoc test results—adjusted p-values and simultaneous confidence intervals. I'll cover both.

Adjusted P-values

The table below displays the six different comparisons in our study, the difference between group means, and the adjusted p-value for each comparison.

```
Tukey Simultaneous Tests for Differences of Means

Difference   Difference       SE of                      Adjusted
Of Levels    of Means     Difference        95% CI       P-Value
B - A          -6.17          2.28     (-12.55,  0.22)     0.061
C - A          -1.75          2.28     ( -8.14,  4.64)     0.868
D - A           3.33          2.28     ( -3.05,  9.72)     0.478
C - B           4.42          2.28     ( -1.97, 10.80)     0.245
D - B           9.50          2.28     (  3.11, 15.89)     0.002
D - C           5.08          2.28     ( -1.30, 11.47)     0.150
```

The adjusted p-value identifies the group comparisons that are significantly different while limiting the family error rate to your significance level. Simply compare the adjusted p-values to your significance level. When adjusted p-values are less than the significance level, the difference between those group means is statistically significant. Importantly, this process controls the family-wise error rate to your significance level. We can be confident that this entire set of comparisons collectively has an error rate of 0.05.

In the output above, only the D − B difference is statistically significant while using a family error rate of 0.05. The mean difference between these two groups is 9.5.

Simultaneous Confidence Intervals

The other way to present post hoc test results is by using simultaneous confidence intervals of the differences between means. In an individual test, the hypothesis test results using a significance level of α are consistent with confidence intervals using a confidence level of $1 - \alpha$. For example, hypothesis tests with a significance level of 0.05 correspond to 95% confidence intervals.

In post hoc tests, we use a simultaneous confidence level rather than an individual confidence level. The simultaneous confidence level applies to the entire family of comparisons. With a 95% simultaneous confidence level, we can be 95% confident that *all* intervals in our set of comparisons contain the actual population differences between groups. A 5% experiment-wise error rate corresponds to 95% simultaneous confidence intervals.

Tukey Simultaneous CIs for our One-Way ANOVA Example

Let's get to the confidence intervals. While the table with the adjusted p-values displays these CIs numerically, I prefer the graph below because it allows for a simple visual assessment, and it provides more information than adjusted p-values.

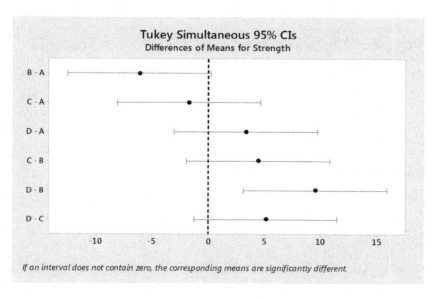

Zero indicates that the group means are equal. When a confidence interval does not contain zero, the difference between that pair of groups is statistically significant. In the chart, only the difference between D − B is significant. These CI results match the hypothesis test results in the previous table. I prefer these CI results because they also provide additional information that the adjusted p-values do not convey.

These confidence intervals provide ranges of values that likely contain the actual population difference between pairs of groups. As with all CIs, the width of the interval for the difference reveals the precision of the estimate. Narrower intervals suggest a more precise estimate. And, you can assess whether the full range of values is practically significant. Remember, statistical significance doesn't necessarily indicate that the results are meaningful in the real world.

When the interval is too wide (imprecise) to be helpful and/or the range includes differences that are not practically significant, you have reason to hesitate before making decisions based on the results.

Post Hoc Tests and the Statistical Power Tradeoff

Post hoc tests are great for controlling the family-wise error rate. Many texts would stop at this point. However, a tradeoff occurs behind the scenes. You need to be aware of it because you might be able to manage it effectively. The tradeoff is the following:

Post hoc tests control the experiment-wise error rate by reducing the statistical power of the comparisons.

Here's how that works and what it means for your study.

To obtain the family error rate you specify, post hoc procedures must lower the significance level for all individual comparisons. For example, to end up with a family error rate of 5% for a set of contrasts, the procedure uses an even lower individual significance level.

As the number of comparisons increases, the post hoc analysis must lower the individual significance level even further. For our six comparisons, Tukey's method uses an individual significance level of approximately 0.011 to produce the family-wise error rate of 0.05. If our ANOVA required more comparisons, it would be even lower.

What's the problem with using a lower individual significance level? Recall the discussion about error rates in chapter 5. Lower significance levels correspond to lower statistical power. If a difference between group means actually exists in the population, a study with lower power is less likely to detect it. You might miss important findings!

Avoiding this power reduction is why many studies use an individual significance level of 0.05 rather than 0.01. Unfortunately, with just four groups, our example post hoc test is forced to use the lower significance level.

Key Takeaway: The more group comparisons you make, the lower the statistical power of those comparisons.

Managing the Power Tradeoff in Post Hoc Tests by Reducing the Number of Comparisons

One method to mitigate this tradeoff is by reducing the number of comparisons. This reduction allows the procedure to use a larger individual error rate to achieve the family error rate that you specify—which increases the statistical power.

Throughout this section, I've written about performing all pairwise comparisons—which compares all possible group pairings. While this is the most common approach, the number of contrasts quickly piles up! However, depending on your study's purpose, you might not need to compare all possible groups.

Your study might need to compare only a subset of all possible comparisons for a variety of reasons. I'll cover two common reasons and show you which post hoc tests you can use. In the following examples, I'll display only the confidence interval graphs and not the hypothesis test results. Notice how these other methods make fewer comparisons (3 and 4) for our example dataset than Tukey's method (6).

While you're designing your study, you must specify the multiple comparisons method you will use. Don't try various methods, and then choose the one that produces the most favorable results. That's data dredging, and it can lead to spurious findings. I'm using multiple post hoc tests on a single dataset to show how they differ, but that's not an appropriate practice for a real study. Define your methodology in advance, including one post hoc analysis, before analyzing the data, and stick to it!

Key Takeaway: When it's possible, compare a subset of groups to increase your statistical power.

Dunnett's Compares Treatments to a Control

If your study has a control group and several treatment groups, you might need to compare the treatment groups only to the control group.

A Control group vs multiple treatment groups

Use Dunnett's method when the following are true:

- Before the study, you know which group (control) you want to compare to all the other groups (treatments).
- You don't need to compare the treatment groups to each other.

Let's use Dunnett's method with our example one-way ANOVA, but we'll tweak the scenario slightly. Suppose we currently use Material A. We performed this experiment to compare the alternative materials (B, C, and D) to it. Material A will be our control group, while the other three are the treatments.

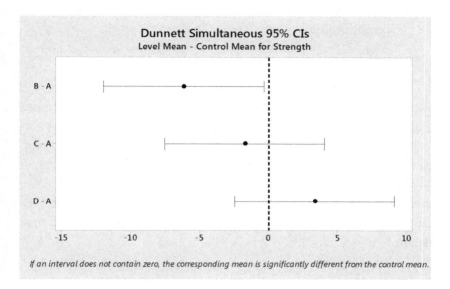

If an interval does not contain zero, the corresponding mean is significantly different from the control mean.

Using Dunnett's method, we see that only the B − A difference is statistically significant because the interval does not include zero. Using Tukey's method, this comparison was not significant. The additional power gained by making fewer comparisons came through for us. On the other hand, unlike Tukey's method, Dunnett's method does not find that the D − B difference is significant because it doesn't compare the treatment groups to each other.

Hsu's MCB to Find the Best

If your study's goal is to identify the best group, you might not need to compare all possible groups. Hsu's Multiple Comparisons to the Best (MCB) identifies the groups that are the best, insignificantly different from the best, and significantly different from the best.

Use Hsu's MCB when you:

- Don't know in advance which group you want to compare to all the other groups.
- Don't need to compare groups that are not the best to other groups that are not the best.
- Can define "the best" as either the group with the highest mean or the lowest mean.

Hsu's MCB compares each group to the group with the best mean (highest or lowest). Using this procedure, you might end up with several groups that are not significantly different than the best group. Keep in mind that the group that is actually best in the entire population might not have the best sample mean due to sampling error. The groups that are not significantly different from the best group might be as good as, or even better than, the group with the best sample mean.

Simultaneous Confidence Intervals for Hsu's MCB

For our one-way ANOVA, we want to use the material that produces the strongest parts. Consequently, we'll use Hsu's MCB and define the highest mean as the best. We don't care about all the other possible comparisons.

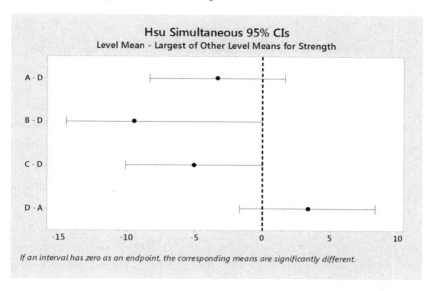

Group D is the best group overall because it has the highest mean (41.07). The procedure compares D to all the other groups. For Hsu's MCB, a group is significantly better than another group when the confidence interval has zero as an endpoint. From the graph, we can see that Material D is significantly better than B and C. However, the A-D comparison contains zero, which indicates that A is not significantly different from the best.

Hsu's MCB determines that the candidates for the best group are A and D. D has the highest sample mean and A is not significantly different from D. On the other hand, the procedure effectively rules out B and C from being the best.

Recap of Using Multiple Comparison Methods

You've seen how the omnibus ANOVA test determines whether means are different in general, but it does not identify specific group differences that are statistically significant.

If you obtain significant ANOVA results, use a post hoc test to explore the mean differences between pairs of groups.

You've also learned how controlling the experiment-wise error rate is a crucial function of these post hoc tests. These family error rates grow at a surprising rate!

Finally, if you don't need to perform all pairwise comparisons, it's worthwhile comparing only a subset because you'll retain more statistical power.

Two-Way ANOVA

Use two-way ANOVA to assess differences between group means that are defined by two categorical factors. Like all hypothesis tests, two-way ANOVA uses sample data to infer the properties of entire population.

To perform this analysis, you'll need two categorical variables, which analysts also refer to as factors. These factors are your independent variables. The number of factors in your analysis determines the name of the ANOVA analysis. One-way ANOVA uses one factor. Two-way ANOVA has two. And, so on. Each factor has a finite number of possible values, which are known as levels. For example, gender is a categorical factor that has the two levels of male and female.

You also need one continuous outcome variable, which is the dependent variable. The various combinations of values for the two categorical variables divide the continuous data into groups. Two-way ANOVA determines whether the mean differences between these groups are statistically significant.

For example, we'll assess whether the two categorical factors of gender and college major correspond to differences in income, a continuous variable.

Additionally, two-way ANOVA determines whether the interaction effect between the two factors is statistically significant. When significant interaction effects are present, it's crucial to interpret them correctly. Because they can be tricky to understand, I'll spend a little extra time covering interaction effects.

Two-way ANOVA begins to touch on aspects of linear least squares models. Consequently, you'll need to assess coefficients, model goodness-of-fit statistics, and residual plots. The complexity increases substantially when you're dealing with significant interaction effects. When using two-way ANOVA, you're starting to enter a different realm than the other hypothesis tests in this book. Consequently, I'll just touch on these issues. However, entire books can be written about linear models, including the one I did write about it!

I'll run through two examples to explain the differences between cases where the interaction effect is and is not significant. Use this CSV dataset for both examples: Two-Way ANOVA. These data are fictional.

Assumptions

For reliable Two-Way ANOVA results, your data should satisfy the following assumptions:

- The outcome or dependent variable is continuous.
- You have two categorical independent variables (factors).

Random residuals with constant variance

In two-way ANOVA, assumptions focus on the residuals rather than the raw data. A residual for an observation in two-way ANOVA equals the actual value of the dependent variable minus the group mean for that observation. In other words, it's the difference between the observed value and the value that the model predicts. Residual plots graph all the residuals for a model, which allows you to evaluate them.

In residual plots, you want to see a random scatter of points around zero and an even spread throughout. If you see patterns or a fanning of values (non-constant variance), the two-way ANOVA models do not satisfy the assumptions. Additionally, look for data points that are far from zero because they are outliers that can significantly affect the results.

This residual plot displays residuals that satisfy the assumptions.

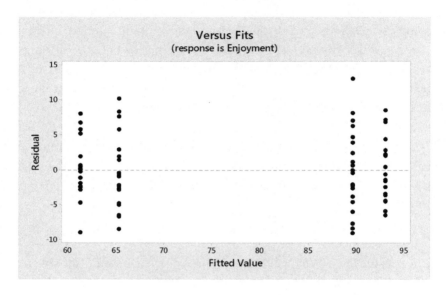

This residual plot is for the condiment enjoyment example in this chapter. There are four bands because the model has four groups, and each group has its own fitted value on the x-axis. These bands all center on zero and have a reasonably constant spread.

Two-Way ANOVA without Interaction

Imagine that we are assessing annual salaries, which is our continuous dependent variable. Our two categorical factors are gender and college major. For this analysis, we'll use the three majors of statistics, psychology, and political science. The combination of these two factors (2 genders X 3 majors) produces the following six groups. Each group contains 20 observations.

Male / Statistics: $77,743	Female / Statistics: $74,074
Male / Psychology: $69,766	Female / Psychology: $65,320
Male/Political Science $62,015	Female/Political Science $55,195

The dollar amount indicates the average income for each group. Two-way ANOVA determines whether the observed differences between means provide strong enough evidence to conclude that the population means are different. Let's perform the analysis!

General Linear Model: Income versus Gender, Major

```
Method

Factor coding   (-1, 0, +1)


Factor Information

Factor   Type  Levels  Values
Gender   Fixed      2  Female, Male
Major    Fixed      3  Political Science, Psychology, Statistics

Analysis of Variance

Source         DF     Adj SS      Adj MS  F-Value  P-Value
  Gender        3  593002242   593002242    25.80    0.000
  Major         2 6009140933  3004570466   130.70    0.000
  Gender*Major  2   88232238    44116119     1.92    0.151
Error         114 2620748173    22989019
Total         119 9311123587


Model Summary

      S   R-sq  R-sq(adj)  R-sq(pred)
4794.69  71.85%     70.62%      68.81%


Coefficients

Term                          Coef  SE Coef  T-Value  P-Value
Constant                     67543      438   154.32    0.000
Gender
  Female                     -2223      438    -5.08    0.000
Major
  Political Science          -8940      619   -14.44    0.000
  Psychology                   574      619     0.93    0.356
Gender*Major
  Female Political Science   -1189      619    -1.92    0.057
  Female Psychology            800      619     1.29    0.199
```

First, look in the P-value column in the Analysis of Variance table. Because the p-values for both Gender and Major are less than our significance level, these factors are statistically significant. These are the main effects in the model.

On the other hand, the interaction effect (Gender*Major) is not significant because its p-value (0.151) is greater than our significance level. Because the interaction effect is not significant, we can focus on only the main effects.

The main effects are the portion of the relationship between an independent variable and the dependent variable that does not change based on the values of the other variables in the model. For example, gender's main effect on average income does not change from one major to another. It's a consistent effect across majors. Males have a higher average income, and that effect is consistent (plus or minus random error) across majors.

In the Coefficients table, each coefficient represents the difference between a categorical value and the overall mean. The corresponding p-value indicates whether that difference is statistically significant. For example, females earn $2,223 less than the overall mean salary. Political science majors earn $8,940 less than the global mean. The p-values indicate these differences are statistically significant. Conversely, psychology majors earn $574 more than the overall mean, but that difference is not significant (0.356).

Each categorical variable must leave out one factor level due to the vagaries of how these coefficient tests work. Consequently, statistics is not under major and males don't appear under gender. The reason is beyond the scope of this book, but I cover it in my *Regression Analysis* book.

The main effects plot graphically represents the group means. Each point on the graph represents a group mean. The lines help indicate whether a main effect is present. Horizontal lines suggest that group means are equal for a factor. Lines that are not horizontal suggest that group means are different across the levels of a factor. Be sure to use this graph in conjunction with the hypothesis test for each factor.

Thanks to the p-values in the ANOVA table, we know that both main effect patterns in this graph are statistically significant. Without the significant test results, the patterns might be attributable to random error.

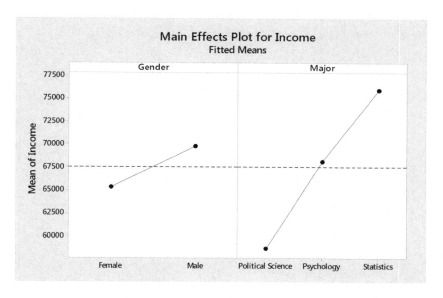

Two-Way ANOVA with Interaction

In the previous example, the interaction effect was not significant. Consequently, it was a simple matter to interpret the main effects. How do you understand interaction effects? To emphasize how these effects work, I'll use an intentionally silly example to make it more intuitive.

Imagine that we're performing a taste test, and the dependent variable is Enjoyment. Our two factors are Food and Condiment. We want to determine which condiment produces the most enjoyment. To keep things simple, we'll include only two foods (ice cream and hot dogs) and two condiments (chocolate sauce and mustard) in our analysis.

I think of interaction effects as an "it depends" effect.

Interaction effects indicate that another variable influences the relationship between an independent and dependent variable. This type of effect makes the model more complex, but if it accurately reflects the real world, it is critical to know how to interpret it. For example, the relationship between condiments and enjoyment probably depends on the type of food.

```
Factor Information

Factor       Type     Levels  Values
Food         Fixed       2    Hot Dog, Ice Cream
Condiment    Fixed       2    Chocolate Sauce, Mustard

Analysis of Variance

Source           DF    Adj SS   Adj MS   F-Value  P-Value
  Food            1       1.6      1.6     0.06    0.801
  Condiment       1     277.5    277.5    11.07    0.001
  Food*Condiment  1   15695.8  15695.8   626.15    0.000
Error            76    1905.1     25.1
Total            79   17880.0


Coefficients

Term                         Coef  SE Coef  T-Value  P-Value
Constant                   77.320    0.560   138.13    0.000
Food
  Hot Dog                   0.141    0.560     0.25    0.801
Condiment
  Chocolate Sauce           1.863    0.560     3.33    0.001
Food*Condiment
  Hot Dog Chocolate Sauce -14.007    0.560   -25.02    0.000
```

First, look in the P-value column in the ANOVA Source of Variation table at the bottom of the output. The p-values indicate that Food is not significant (p = 0.801), while Condiment is statistically significant (p = 0.001). These are the main effects. The significance of Condiment suggests that a portion of the relationship between Condiment and

Enjoyment does not change based on the value of the other independent variable.

However, the extremely low p-value (0.000) for the interaction effect is also statistically significant. In general, interaction effects indicate that the relationship between an independent variable and a dependent variable changes based on the value of another variable.

For our ANOVA model, the significant interaction indicates that the relationship between Condiment and Enjoyment *depends* on the type of food. That makes sense when you think about it. You might like chocolate sauce quite a bit, but I bet you'd find it disgusting on hot dogs!

Interaction Effects in Depth

If only the main effects are significant, you'd be able to state that either chocolate sauce or mustard always increased your satisfaction the most and by a consistent amount regardless of the food. But that's not how it works with food and condiments!

When you have statistically significant interaction effects, you can't interpret the main effects without considering the interactions. In the previous example, you can't answer the question about which condiment is better without knowing the type of food. Sometimes mustard is better while other times chocolate sauce is better. Again, "it depends."

It's often easiest to interpret an interaction effect using specialized plots known as interaction plots. On interaction plots, crossing lines indicate the possible presence of an interaction effect, while parallel lines suggest there is no interaction effect. Again, use this plot in conjunction with the appropriate hypothesis test to help ensure that the patterns you see are not random error.

Thanks to the p-values in the ANOVA table, we know that the inter-action effect pattern in this graph is statistically significant.

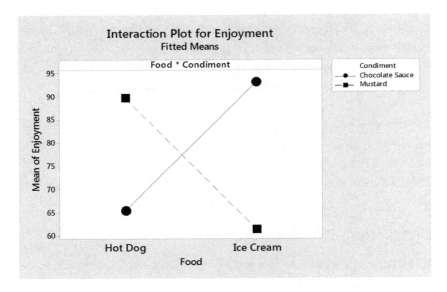

The hot dog/mustard group and the ice cream/chocolate sauce group have relatively high enjoyment scores. Conversely, the hot dog/choc-olate sauce group and the ice cream/mustard group have lower scores. That makes sense intuitively. However, to explain the changing rela-tionship between Condiment and Enjoyment statistically, you must include the interaction effect. Otherwise, your model might tell you to put chocolate sauce on your hot dog!

Review and Next Steps

In this chapter, we covered ANOVA and the F-test to learn how to compare the means of three or more groups.

One-way ANOVA uses one categorical variable to define the groups that you compare. Two-way ANOVA, surprise, uses two categorical variables to define these groups.

ANOVA is an omnibus test that only indicates whether you have enough evidence to conclude that not all means are equal. If you want to determine which specific pairs of groups are significantly different, use post hoc tests. However, remember to reduce the number of comparisons when possible to preserve statistical power.

We have the mean well covered by now! In the next chapter, we'll assess other characteristics of continuous data, such as variability, correlations, and the distribution of values.

CHAPTER 10

Continuous Data: Variability, Correlations, Distributions & Outliers

As you saw in chapter 8, continuous data have a more extensive range of properties than other data types. So far, we've looked at analyzing means extensively. Recall that the sample mean is an estimate of the population mean, which is the parameter μ (mu).

However, you can use samples of continuous data to estimate other population parameters, such as the population standard deviation (σ, sigma) and the correlation between variables (ρ, rho). Like the population mean, these other parameters are generally unknowable, but we can use samples and hypothesis testing to draw conclusions about them.

Continuous data can also follow a wide range of possible distributions. The bell-shaped normal distribution is just one of many possible distributions. Fortunately, hypothesis tests can help you determine whether your data follow the normal distribution or some other distribution.

We'll start by testing variability, move on to testing correlations, and then test the distribution of a sample dataset. Finally, I'll close the chapter by talking about outliers and the problems they pose for continuous data.

Testing Variability

Variance tests assess the variability of the data in multiple groups to determine whether they are different. Variance is a measure of variability that uses squared units, making it hard for us humans to interpret. However, various statistical procedures include variances in their calculations. Fortunately, statistical software can convert the results to standard deviations, which are easier to understand because they use the same units as the original data. The standard deviation is simply the square root of the variances.

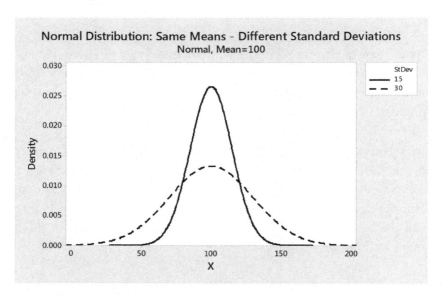

Like all hypothesis tests, variance tests use sample data to infer the properties of entire populations. Do the populations have different spreads?

Why would you want to compare population variances? When you are assessing processes, you might want to identify a process that produces more consistent products (i.e., less variable). That's good for quality control! Additionally, you can use these tests in conjunction with 2-sample t-tests and ANOVA to determine whether your data satisfy the assumptions about equal variances.

Like t-tests for means, variance tests come in several flavors. These include one-sample and two-sample tests. There are even versions that let you compare more than two groups. We'll stick with the one and two sample versions, but you can apply the following information to more than two groups.

One-Sample Variance Test

Use the one-sample variance test to compare your sample standard deviation to a hypothesized value for the population. Typically, researchers use a value that is meaningful for their study. This value forms the null hypothesis for the test. The procedure also creates a confidence interval of likely values for the population standard deviation.

Please note that with a 1 Variance test, you don't need to perform the hypothesis test. If you just want to understand the estimate's precision, assess the confidence interval to identify the range of likely values. That information can be valuable even when you don't have a reference or hypothesized value.

The 1-sample variance test has the following hypotheses:

- **Null hypothesis:** The population standard deviation equals the hypothesized standard deviation.
- **Alternative hypothesis:** The population standard deviation does not equal the hypothesized standard deviation.

If the p-value is less than your significance level (e.g., 0.05), you can reject the null hypothesis. The difference between the population standard deviation and the hypothesized standard deviation is statistically significant. Your sample provides strong enough evidence to conclude that the population standard deviation does not equal the hypothesized value.

Assumptions

For reliable 1-sample variance test results, your data should satisfy the following assumptions:

- Random sample
- Continuous data

Your sample data should follow a normal distribution or have more than 40 observations

If your data follow the normal distribution, use the Chi-square method. If your sample size is greater than 40 and your data are skewed, use Bonett's method. If you have skewed data and fewer than 40 observations, the test will have a Type I error rate higher than your significance level. See Testing Methods for more information.

Example 1 Variance Test

A manufacturing company is testing the strength of a material. From experience, analysts know that if the variability is too high, it causes product failures. They require a consistent strength for product reliability. The quality analysts randomly select 20 samples of the material and measure its strength. They perform a 1 Variance test and compare the sample standard deviation to a reference value of 5. If the population standard deviation is greater than this value, the variability is too high.

Let's analyze the data! Use the CSV data file: ProductStrength.

Test and CI for One Variance: Strength

```
Method

Null hypothesis        σ = 5
Alternative hypothesis  σ ≠ 5

The chi-square method is only for the normal distribution.
The Bonett method is for any continuous distribution.


Statistics

Variable   N   StDev  Variance
Strength   20  10.1        101


95% Confidence Intervals

                        CI for        CI for
Variable   Method        StDev       Variance
Strength   Chi-Square   (7.7, 14,7)  (59,   216)
           Bonett       (7.5, 15.0)  (56,   225)


Tests

                         Test
Variable   Method      Statistic  DF  P-Value
Strength   Chi-Square     77.06   19   0.000
           Bonett           -      -   0.000
```

The output indicates that the sample standard deviation is 10.1, which is higher than the reference value of 5.

If the p-value is less than your significance level, the difference between the standard deviation and reference value is statistically significant. This test produces several p-values because it presents the results for several methods. The correct method depends on the characteristics of your data. In many cases, the different p-values yield the same test conclusion. However, if they differ, you'll need to determine which p-value is correct for your data.

Because both p-values (0.000) are less than the standard significance level of 0.05, we reject the null hypothesis. If the p-value is low, the null must go! Our sample data provide enough evidence to support the hypothesis that the population standard is greater than 5. This result indicates that the strength of the material is too inconsistent to be usable.

Furthermore, the confidence interval estimates that the standard deviation for the entire population is likely between 7.5 and 15. The confidence interval excludes the reference value of 5, which is why we can conclude that the population standard deviation is different from that value.

Two-Sample Variances Test

Use the two-sample variances test to determine whether two population standard deviations are different and to create a confidence interval of the difference between groups. This test uses independent samples. In other words, each group contains different people or items.

The hypotheses for the 2-sample variances test are the following:

- **Null hypothesis:** The standard deviations for the two populations are equal.
- **Alternative hypothesis:** The standard deviations for the two populations are not equal.

If the p-value is less than your significance level (e.g., 0.05), you can reject the null hypothesis. The difference between the two standard deviations is statistically significant. Your sample provides strong enough evidence to conclude that the two population standard deviations are not equal.

Assumptions

For reliable 2-sample variances test results, your data should satisfy the following assumptions:

- Random sample

- Continuous data
- Independent groups

Your sample data should follow a normal distribution or each group is unimodal and has more than 20 observations

If your sample size is greater than 20 in each group, Bonett's method produces valid results even with moderately skewed data. If you have very skewed data or a smaller sample size, use Levene's method. If your data follows the normal distribution very closely, use the F-test. The F-test is the most powerful method, but it is susceptible to small departures from the normal distribution. See Testing Methods for more information.

Example of the 2 Variances Test

For this example, I'll use data from a Mythbusters' Battle of the Sexes episode. In that episode, the Mythbusters evaluate whether men or women are better at parallel parking.

The Mythbusters have ten subjects per group and use a parking test that produces scores between 0 and 100. The mean difference between men and women is not statistically significant.

However, while testing the subjects, the hosts noticed that the women's parallel parking skills appear to be more variable than the men's abilities. Graphing the data shows how women have a broader range of scores than men.

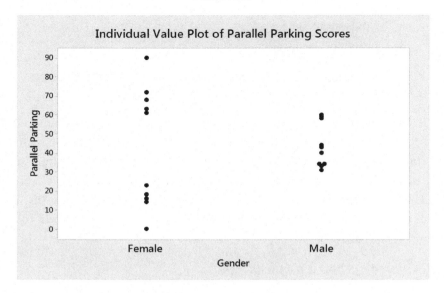

While the spread of these two groups looks very different, let's use the 2 Variances test to determine whether this difference is statistically significant. Use the CSV file that contains the data for this example: VariancesTest.

```
Tests

                                              Test
Method                           DF1  DF2  Statistic  P-Value
F Test (normal)                    9    9       7.48    0.006
Levene's Test (any continuous)     1   18      27.04    0.000
```

The p-value is 0.000, which is less than any reasonable significance level. The sample evidence is strong enough to reject the null hypothesis and conclude that women are more variable at parallel parking than men.

Variances Testing Methods

In the output for the variance tests, you might have noticed different p-values for different testing methods. There are several types of variances tests that use alternative methods to assess your data. While the hypotheses and the interpretation of p-values remain the same, the different tests use different calculations. These tests often agree, but when they disagree, it's good to know which one is best for your data. These tests can have restrictions on the number of groups and data distributions. Use the following information to decide:

F-test: 2 groups. We covered the F-test in ANOVA when comparing means. However, you can also use it to compare variances when you have two groups. The F-test is often more powerful than the other tests. However, in this context, the F-test is very sensitive to departures from normality. If you aren't sure your data are normally distributed, use one of the other tests.

Bonett's Test: This test is usually more powerful than Levene's test. Use this test unless you have a small sample and/or a very skewed distribution. Under these conditions, Bonett's test has a higher Type I error rate than the significance level.

Levene's Test: Use this test when you have fewer than 20 observations in a group or a group is very skewed. This method also works with more than two groups.

Bartlett's Test: At least two groups. Like the F-test, it is sensitive to even slight departures from normality.

Chi-square method: 1 group. Use this method when you have one group and it follows the normal distribution. If your single group doesn't follow the normal distribution, use Bonett's test.

Test of Pearson's Correlation

My *Introduction to Statistics* book thoroughly covers how to interpret correlation coefficients, from -1 to +1. Here, I present an interpretation for just one dataset. Because this book is about hypothesis tests, I will focus on the hypothesis test associated with correlation coefficients. What does a statistically significant correlation indicate?

This hypothesis test determines whether the correlation you see in your sample exists in the population. The hypotheses for Pearson's correlations are the following:

- **Null**: There is no correlation between the variables ($\rho = 0$).
- **Alternative**: There is a correlation between the variables ($\rho \neq 0$).

In the null hypothesis, a correlation coefficient of zero indicates that no correlation exists. In other words, knowing the value of one variable provides no information about the value of the other variable. As one variable increases, the other variable does not tend to increase or decrease.

For the alternative hypothesis, a non-zero correlation coefficient indicates that the value of one variable provides information about the likely value of the other variable—a correlation exists. As the value of one variable increases, the other variable's value tends to either increase or decrease at a predictable rate. Note that this is a two-tailed test so it can detect both positive and negative correlations. Hence, the "does not equal" wording in the alternative hypothesis.

If the p-value is less than your significance level (e.g., 0.05), you can reject the null hypothesis. The correlation coefficient is statistically significant. Your sample provides strong enough evidence to conclude that the population correlation coefficient does not equal zero.

Assumptions

Pearson's correlation describes linear relationships between two continuous variables. Other types of correlation/association with their own set of assumptions exist for different kinds of data.

For reliable Pearson's correlation test results, your data should satisfy the following assumptions:

- Two continuous variables
- Linear relationship
- Outliers have a considerable influence on the results

Data follow a bivariate normal distribution or you have at least 25 observation

If you have at least 25 observations, p-values are valid for data that depart from the normal distribution. With fewer observations, p-values might not be accurate for nonnormal distributions.

Example of Correlation Hypothesis Test

Let's return to the height and weight example. The graph and statistical output are below.

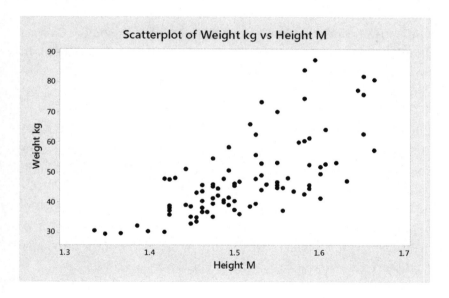

Correlation: Height M, Weight kg

```
Pearson correlation of Height M and Weight kg = 0.694
P-Value = 0.000
```

The correlation for these data is 0.694. It's a positive value, which indicates that as height increases, weight tends to increase. You can see that relationship in the graph. The strength of the correlation is moderate. It's not so strong that the data points are tightly hugging a line. However, it's not so weak that it looks like an amorphous blob.

The p-value of 0.000 is less than our significance level of 0.05. The sample evidence is strong enough to reject the null hypothesis and conclude that the correlation exists in the population.

Testing the Distribution of Your Continuous Data

You're probably familiar with data that follow the normal distribution. The normal distribution is a probability distribution that creates a nice, familiar bell-shaped curve. Unfortunately, not all data are normally distributed or as intuitive to understand. You can picture the symmetric normal distribution, but what about the Weibull or Gamma distributions? This uncertainty might leave you feeling unsettled. In this section, I show you how to identify the probability distribution of your data.

You might think of nonnormal data as abnormal. However, in some areas, you should expect nonnormal distributions. For instance, income data are typically right-skewed. If a process has a natural limit, data tend to skew away from the boundary. For example, purity can't be higher than 100%, which might cause the data to cluster near the upper limit and skew left towards lower values. On the other hand, drill holes can't be smaller than the drill bit. The sizes of the drill holes might be right-skewed away from the minimum possible size.

 Normal

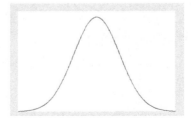

Right-Skewed

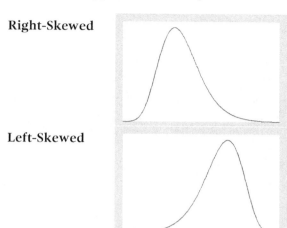

Left-Skewed

Data that follow any probability distribution can be valuable. These distributions allow us to quantify probabilities for ranges of values. However, many people don't feel as comfortable with nonnormal data. Let's shed light on how to identify the distribution of your data!

There is a wide variety of probability distributions that can fit many distribution shapes. How do we know which distribution is the correct one? How do we know whether our data follow the normal distribution? Fortunately, we can use special hypothesis tests that test the distribution of your data.

The normality test is just one of such tests. A normality test determines whether your data substantially deviates from the normal distribution. There are other tests for the other distributions as well. For example, the Weibull test evaluates if your data deviation from that distribution. Same for the exponential, gamma, and logistic distribution tests among others.

We'll learn how to identify the probability distribution using body fat percentage data from middle school girls that I collected during an experiment. Analyze the CSV data file: body_fat.

Graph the Raw Data

Let's plot the raw data to visualize it.

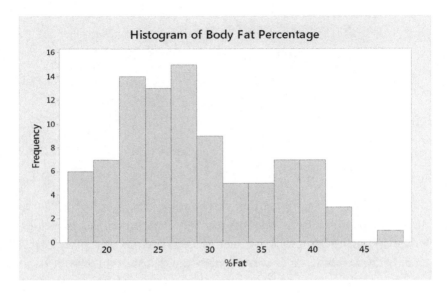

The histogram gives us a good overview of the data. At a glance, we can see that these data clearly are not normally distributed. They are right-skewed. The peak is around 27%, and the distribution extends further into the higher values than to the lower values.

These data don't look normal. If they're not normal, which probability distribution do they follow? Fortunately, hypothesis tests can help us!

Using Distribution Tests

Distribution tests are hypothesis tests that determine whether your random sample data were drawn from a population that follows a hypothesized probability distribution. Like any hypothesis test, distribution tests have a null hypothesis and an alternative hypothesis.

- **Null:** The sample data follow the hypothesized distribution.
- **Alternative:** The sample data do not follow the hypothesized distribution.

For distribution tests, small p-values indicate that you can reject the null hypothesis and conclude that your data were not drawn from a population with the specified distribution. However, we want to identify the probability distribution that our data follow rather than the distributions they don't follow! Consequently, distribution tests are a rare case where you look for high p-values to identify candidate distributions.

Before we test our data to identify the distribution, here are some measures you need to know:

Anderson-Darling statistic (AD): There are different distribution tests. The test I'll use for our data is the Anderson-Darling test. The Anderson-Darling statistic is the test statistic. It's like the t-value for t-tests or the F-value for F-tests. Typically, you don't interpret this statistic directly, but the software uses it to calculate the p-value for the test.

P-value: Distribution tests that have high p-values are suitable candidates for your data's distribution. Unfortunately, it is not possible to calculate p-values for some distributions with three parameters.

LRT P: If you are considering a three-parameter distribution, assess the LRT P to determine whether the third parameter significantly improves the fit compared to the associated two-parameter distribution. An LRT P-value that is less than your significance level indicates a significant improvement over the two-parameter distribution. If you see a higher value, consider staying with the two-parameter distribution.

Normality Test

Analysts often perform a normality test because some hypothesis tests assume your data follow a normal distribution. Although, as you've learned, you can waive the normality assumption when your sample size is large enough thanks to the central limit theorem. I suspect that analysts worry too much about the normal assumption and use the normality test unnecessarily. At any rate, let's test our data.

The normality test has the following hypotheses:

- **Null**: The sample data follow the normal distribution.
- **Alternative**: The sample data do not follow the normal distribution.

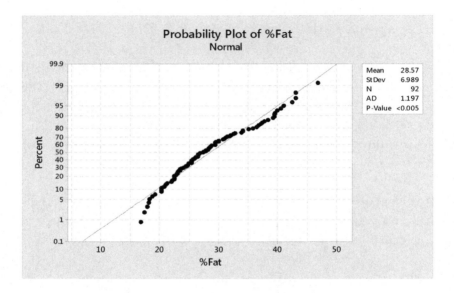

For now, the primary portion of the output we'll assess is the p-value. Because it is very low, the null must go! We can reject the null hypothesis that these data follow the normal distribution. We'll interpret the graph portion in more detail later, but if the data had fit the normal distribution, the points would follow the straight line more closely.

Okay, so our data don't follow the normal distribution, which distribution do they fit?

Goodness-of-Fit Tests for Other Distributions

I'm using Minitab, which can test 14 probability distributions and two transformations all at once. Each distribution test is similar to the normality test, except it's testing a different distribution. Using other software, you might need to assess the fit of each distribution individually.

Let's look at the output. We're looking for the highest p-values in the Goodness-of-Fit Test table. The higher p-values identify candidate distributions for us to consider.

```
Goodness of Fit Test

Distribution              AD         P    LRT P
Normal                  1.197   <0.005
Box-Cox Transformation  0.406    0.345
Lognormal               0.406    0.345
3-Parameter Lognormal   0.331       *    0.486
Exponential            24.618   <0.003
2-Parameter Exponential 6.100   <0.010    0.000
Weibull                 1.466   <0.010
3-Parameter Weibull     0.303   >0.500    0.000
Smallest Extreme Value  2.954   <0.010
Largest Extreme Value   0.321   >0.250
Gamma                   0.594    0.135
3-Parameter Gamma       0.308       *    0.097
Logistic                1.106   <0.005
Loglogistic             0.513    0.153
3-Parameter Loglogistic 0.393       *    0.303
Johnson Transformation  0.268    0.677
```

In the first line, we see the normality test results again. We have nonnormal data.

The Box-Cox transformation and the Johnson transformation both have high p-values. If we need to transform our data to follow the normal distribution, the high p-values indicate that we can use these transformations successfully. However, we'll disregard the transformations because we want to identify the probability distribution of our raw data rather than transforming it.

The highest p-value is for the three-parameter Weibull distribution (>0.500). For the three-parameter Weibull, the LRT P is significant (0.000), which means that the third parameter significantly improves the fit.

The lognormal distribution has the next highest p-value of 0.345.

Let's consider the three-parameter Weibull distribution and lognormal distribution to be our top two candidates.

Using Probability Plots

Probability plots might be the best way to determine whether your data follow a particular distribution. If your data follow the straight line on the graph, the distribution fits your data. This process is simple to do visually. Informally, this process is called the "fat pencil" test. If all the data points line up within the area of a fat pencil laid over the center straight line, you can conclude that your data follow the distribution.

These plots are especially useful in cases where the distribution tests are too powerful. Distribution tests are like other hypothesis tests. As the sample size increases, the statistical power of the test also increases. With very large sample sizes, the test can have so much power that trivial departures from the distribution produce statistically significant results. In these cases, your p-value will be less than the significance level even when your data follow the distribution.

The solution is to assess the probability plots to identify the distribution of your data. If the data points fall along the straight line, you can conclude the data follow that distribution even if the p-value is statistically significant.

The probability plots include the normal distribution, our top two candidates, and the gamma distribution.

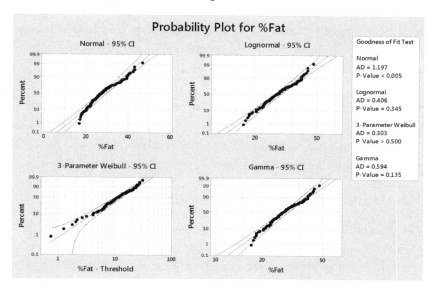

The data points for the normal distribution don't follow the center-line. However, the data points do follow the line very closely for both the lognormal and the three-parameter Weibull distributions. The gamma distribution doesn't follow the centerline quite as well as the other two, and its p-value is lower. Again, it appears like the choice comes down to our top two candidates from before. How do we choose?

Three-Parameter Distributions

Three-parameter distributions have a threshold parameter. The threshold parameter is also known as the location parameter. This parameter shifts the entire distribution left and right along the x-axis. The threshold/location parameter defines the smallest possible value in the distribution. You should use a three-parameter distribution only if the location truly is the lowest possible value. In other words, use subject-area knowledge to help you choose.

The threshold parameter for our data is 16.06038 (shown in the next table). This cutoff point is based on (but not equal to) the smallest value in our sample. However, in the full population of middle school girls, it is unlikely that there is a strict cutoff at this value. Instead, lower values are possible even though they are less likely. Consequently, I'll pick the lognormal distribution.

Using p-values and probability plots, we were able to narrow the distributions down to the top two candidates. Then we used subject area knowledge to pick between those two. The best statistical analyses combine proper interpretation with subject area knowledge.

Parameter Values for Our Distribution

We've identified our distribution as the lognormal distribution. Now, we need to find the parameter values for it. Population parameters are the values that define the shape and location of the distribution. We just need to look at the distribution parameters table!

```
ML Estimates of Distributions Parameters

Distribution                Location    Shape     Scale    Threshold
Normal*                     28.56522             6.98923
Box-Cox Transformation*      3.32317             0.24188
Lognormal*                   3.32317             0.24188
3-Parameter Lognormal        3.04855             0.31575   6.41648
Exponential                                     28.56522
2-Parameter Exponential                         11.89449  16.67071
Weibull                                4.35553  31.31946
3-Parameter Weibull                    1.85718  14.07043  16.06038
Smallest Extreme Value      32.19748             7.29878
Largest Extreme Value       25.28363             5.72752
Gamma                                 17.39341   1.64230
3-Parameter Gamma                      5.10385   3.13720  12.55290
Logistic                    28.05381             4.04055
Loglogistic                  3.31872             0.14150
3-Parameter Loglogistic      2.86738             0.22260   9.80521
Johnson Transformation*      0.04555             0.97553
```

Our body fat percentage data for middle school girls follow a lognormal distribution with a location of 3.32317 and a scale of 0.24188.

I created a probability distribution plot of our two top candidates using the parameter estimates. Notice how the three-parameter Weibull distribution stops abruptly at the threshold/location value. However, the lognormal distribution continues to lower values.

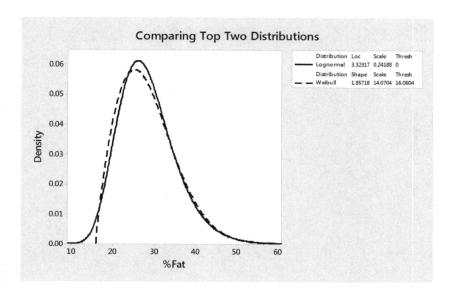

Identifying the probability distribution that your data follow can be critical for analyses that are very sensitive to the distribution, such as capability analysis.

Finally, I'll close this section with a graph that compares the raw data to the fitted distribution that we identified.

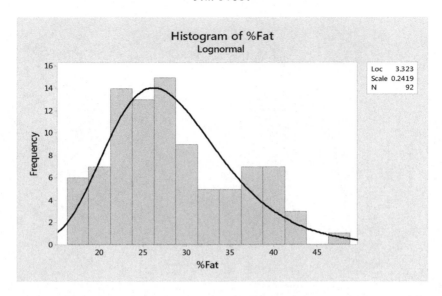

Caution: What These Tests Do NOT Tell You!

Throughout this book, we looked at different ways to test the equality of group means—t-tests, ANOVA, and post hoc tests. We also assessed the variability and distribution of continuous data. These approaches produce estimates of population means (μ), standard deviations (σ), and confidence intervals that are likely to contain the population parameters.

Individually, these parameter estimates and distribution properties can help us make decisions. However, sometimes we need an analysis that ties all of this information together and indicates where individual values are likely to fall. In certain circumstances, knowing the proportion of values that fall within specified intervals is crucial.

For example, the length of a part must fall within spec limits, or it is defective. Even when the mean length falls within the spec limit, it's possible that variability is too high and many part lengths fall outside the spec limits, as shown in the graph.

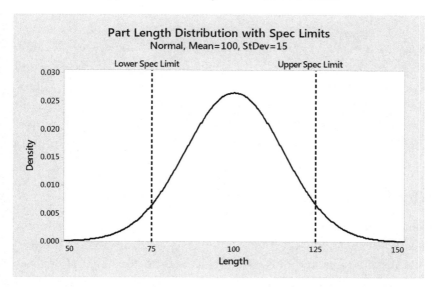

Part Length Distribution with Spec Limits
Normal, Mean=100, StDev=15

Excessive variability can cause a costly number of product defects even when the mean is acceptable. Consequently, it can be vital to assess the mean, variability, and distribution of values jointly.

There are specialized analyses that do just that, but they go beyond the scope of this book. However, I want to mention them so you know they exist. To better understand the distribution of individual values rather than the population parameters, use the following analyses:

Tolerance intervals: A tolerance interval is a range that likely contains a specific proportion of a population. For our example, we might want to know the range where 99% of the population falls for the part lengths. We can compare the tolerance interval to our requirements to determine whether there is too much variability.

Capability analysis: This type of analysis uses sample data to determine how effectively a process produces output with characteristics that fall within the spec limits. These tools incorporate the center, spread, and distribution of your data to estimate the proportion of defects.

While I don't cover these two analyses, you should know enough about parameter estimates, identifying probability distributions, and using probability distributions to understand the principles of how they work. For instance, in the previous graph, parts with lengths less than 75 and greater than 125 are defective. By knowing the normal distribution that part lengths follow, you can calculate the proportion of parts in those regions!

Outliers

Outliers are unusual values in your dataset, and they can distort statistical analyses and violate their assumptions, such as creating nonnormal distributions and unequal variances. Unfortunately, all analysts will confront outliers and be forced to decide what to do with them. Given the problems they can cause, you might think that it's best to remove them from your data. But, that's not always the case. Removing outliers is legitimate only for specific reasons.

Outliers are a simple concept—they are values that are notably different from other data points, and they can cause problems in statistical procedures.

To demonstrate how much a single outlier can affect the results, let's examine the properties of an example dataset. It contains 15 height measurements of human males. One of those values is an outlier. The table shows the mean height and standard deviation with and without the outlier.

Throughout this section, I'll use this example CSV dataset: Outliers.

With Outlier	Without Outlier	Difference
2.4m (7' 10.5")	1.8m (5' 10.8")	0.6m (~2 feet)
2.3m (7' 6")	0.14m (5.5 inches)	2.16m (~7 feet)

From the table, it's easy to see how a single outlier can distort reality. A single value changes the mean height by 0.6m (2 feet) and the standard deviation by a whopping 2.16m (7 feet)! Hypothesis tests that use the mean with the outlier are off the mark. And, the much larger standard deviation will severely reduce statistical power!

Before performing statistical analyses, you should identify potential outliers and figure out what to do with them.

Outliers can be very informative about the subject-area and data collection process. It's essential to understand how outliers occur and whether they might happen again as a normal part of the process or study area. Unfortunately, resisting the temptation to remove outliers inappropriately can be difficult. Outliers increase the variability in your data, which decreases statistical power. Consequently, excluding outliers can cause your results to become statistically significant. Deciding how to handle outliers depends on investigating their underlying cause.

In this section, I'll help you decide whether you should remove outliers from your dataset, how to identify outliers, and how to analyze your data when you can't remove them. The proper action depends on what causes the outliers. In broad strokes, there are three causes for outliers—data entry or measurement errors, sampling problems and unusual conditions, and natural variation.

Let's go over these three causes!

Data Entry and Measurement Errors and Outliers

Errors can occur during measurement and data entry. During data entry, typos can produce weird values. Imagine that we're measuring the height of adult men and gather the following dataset.

Height M
1.5895
1.6508
1.7131
1.7136
1.7212
1.7296
1.7343
1.7663
1.8018
1.8394
1.8869
1.9357
1.9482
2.1038
10.8135

In this dataset, the value of 10.8135 is clearly an outlier. Not only does it stand out, but it's an impossible height value. Examining the numbers more closely, we conclude the zero might have been accidental. Hopefully, we can either go back to the original record or even re-measure the subject to determine the correct height.

These types of errors are easy cases to understand. If you determine that an outlier value is an error, correct the value when possible. That can involve fixing the typo or possibly remeasuring the item or person. If that's not possible, you must delete the data point because you know it's an incorrect value.

Sampling Problems Can Cause Outliers

Inferential statistics use samples to draw conclusions about a specific population. Studies should carefully define a population, and then draw a random sample from it specifically. That's the process by which a study can learn about a population.

Unfortunately, your study might accidentally obtain an item or person that is not from the target population. There are several ways this can occur. For example, unusual events or characteristics can occur that deviate from the defined population. Perhaps the experimenter measures the item or subject under abnormal conditions. In other cases, you can accidentally collect an item that falls outside your target population, and, thus, it might have unusual characteristics.

Let's bring this to life with several examples!

Suppose a study assesses the strength of a product. The researchers define the population as the output of the standard manufacturing process. The normal process includes standard materials, manufacturing settings, and conditions. If something unusual happens during a portion of the study, such as a power failure or a machine setting drifting off the standard value, it can affect the products.

These abnormal manufacturing conditions can cause outliers by creating products with atypical strength values. Products manufactured under these unusual conditions do not reflect your target population of products from the normal process. Consequently, you can legitimately remove these data points from your dataset.

During a bone density study that I participated in as a scientist, I noticed an outlier in the bone density growth for a subject. Her growth value was very unusual. The study's subject coordinator discovered that the subject had diabetes, which affects bone health. Our study's goal was to model bone density growth in pre-adolescent girls with no health conditions that affect bone growth. Consequently, her data were excluded from our analyses because she was not a member of our target population.

If you can establish that an item or person does not represent your target population, you can remove that data point. However, you must be able to attribute a specific cause or reason for why that sample item does not fit your target population.

Natural Variation Can Produce Outliers

The previous causes of outliers are bad things. They represent different types of problems that you need to correct. However, natural variation can also produce outliers—and it's not necessarily a problem.

All data distributions have a spread of values. Extreme values can occur, but they have lower probabilities. If your sample size is large enough, you're bound to obtain unusual values. In a normal distribution, approximately 1 in 370 observations will be at least three standard deviations away from the mean. However, random chance might include extreme values in smaller datasets! In other words, the process or population you're studying might produce weird values naturally. There's nothing wrong with these data points. They're unusual, but they are a normal part of the data distribution.

For example, I fit a model that uses historical U.S. Presidential approval ratings to predict how later historians would ultimately rank each President. It turns out a President's lowest approval rating predicts the historian ranks. However, one data point severely affects the model. President Truman doesn't fit the model. He had an abysmal lowest approval rating of 22%, but later historians gave him a relatively good rank of #6. If I remove that single observation, the regression model fits the data so much better!

However, there was no justifiable reason to remove that point. While it was an oddball, it accurately reflects the potential surprises and uncertainty inherent in the political system. If I remove it, the model makes the process appear more predictable than it actually is. Even though this unusual observation is influential, I left it in the model. It's bad practice to remove data points simply to produce a better fitting model or statistically significant results.

If the extreme value is a legitimate observation that is a natural part of the population you're studying, you should leave it in the dataset. I'll explain how to analyze datasets that contain outliers you can't exclude shortly!

Guidelines for Removing Outliers

Sometimes it's best to keep outliers in your data. They can capture valuable information that is part of your study area. Retaining these points can be hard, particularly when it reduces statistical significance! However, excluding extreme values solely due to their extremeness can distort the results by removing information about the variability inherent in the study area. You're forcing the subject area to appear less variable than it is in reality.

When considering whether to remove an outlier, you'll need to evaluate if it appropriately reflects your target population, subject-area, research question, and research methodology. Did anything unusual happen while measuring these observations, such as power failures, abnormal experimental conditions, or anything else out of the norm? Is there anything substantially different about an observation, whether it's a person, item, or transaction? Did measurement or data entry errors occur?

If the outlier in question is:

- A measurement error or data entry error, correct the error if possible. If you can't fix it, remove that observation because you know it's incorrect.
- Not a part of the population you are studying (i.e., unusual properties or conditions), you can legitimately remove the outlier.
- A natural part of the population you are studying, you should not remove it.

When you decide to remove outliers, document the excluded data points and explain your reasoning. You must be able to attribute a specific cause for removing outliers. Another approach is to perform the analysis with and without these observations and discuss the differences. Comparing results in this manner is particularly useful when you're unsure about removing an outlier and when there is substantial disagreement within a group over this question.

Five Ways to Find Outliers

Now you have an understanding of what to consider while investigating outliers and how to decide when to remove them. But what are the best ways to find these unusual values to investigate?

Unfortunately, there are no strict statistical rules for definitively identifying outliers. Finding outliers depends on subject-area knowledge and an understanding of the data collection process. While there is no solid mathematical definition, there are guidelines, graphs, and statistical tests you can use to find outlier candidates.

In this section, I present various methods for finding them and share my preferred approach. There are a variety of ways to find outliers. All these methods employ different strategies for finding values that are unusual compared to the rest of the dataset. I'll start with visual assessments and then move onto more analytical assessments.

Let's find that outlier! I've got five methods for you to try.

Sorting Your Datasheet to Find Outliers

Sorting your datasheet is a simple but effective way to highlight unusual values. Simply sort your data sheet for each variable and then look for unusually high or low values.

For example, I've sorted the example dataset in ascending order. The highest value is clearly different than the others. While this approach doesn't quantify the outlier's degree of unusualness, I like it because, at a glance, you'll find the unusually high or low values.

Height M
1.5895
1.6508
1.7131
1.7136
1.7212
1.7296
1.7343
1.7663
1.8018
1.8394
1.8869
1.9357
1.9482
2.1038
10.8135

Graphing Your Data to Identify Outliers

Boxplots, histograms, and scatterplots can highlight outliers.

Boxplots display asterisks on the graph to indicate when datasets contain outliers. These graphs use the interquartile method with fences to find outliers, which I explain later. The boxplot displays our example dataset. It's clear that the outlier is quite different than the typical data value.

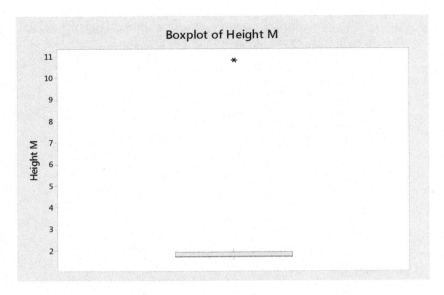

You can also use boxplots to find outliers when you have groups in your data. The boxplot below shows a different dataset that has an outlier in the Method 2 group.

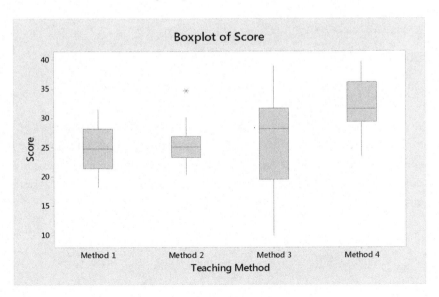

Histograms also emphasize the existence of outliers. Look for isolated bars. Our outlier is the bar far to the right. The graph crams the legitimate data points on the far left.

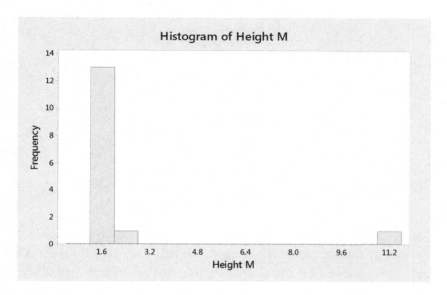

Most of the outliers I discuss are univariate outliers. We look at a data distribution for a single variable and find values that fall outside the distribution. However, you can use a scatterplot to detect outliers in a multivariate setting.

In the next graph, we're looking at two variables, Input and Output. The scatterplot with regression line shows how most of the points follow the fitted line for the model. However, the circled point does not fit the model well.

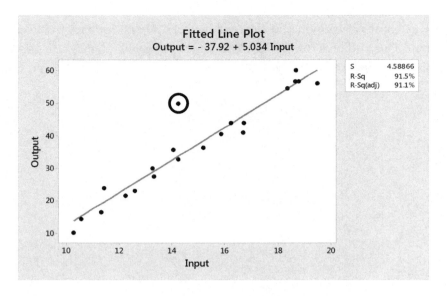

Interestingly, the Input value (~14) for this observation isn't unusual because the other Input values range from 10 through 20 on the X-axis. Also, notice how the Output value (~50) is similarly within the range of values on the Y-axis (10 – 60). Neither the Input nor the Output values themselves are unusual in this dataset. Instead, it's an outlier because it doesn't fit the model.

This type of outlier can be a problem in regression analysis. Given the multifaceted nature of multivariate regression, there are numerous types of outliers in that realm. In my book about regression analysis, I detail various methods and tests for identifying outliers in a multivariate context.

Using Z-scores to Detect Outliers

Z-scores can quantify the unusualness of an observation when your data follow the normal distribution. Z-scores are the number of standard deviations above and below the mean that each value falls. For example, a Z-score of 2 indicates that an observation is two standard deviations above the average. Conversely, a Z-score of -2 signifies it is two standard deviations below the mean. A Z-score of zero represents a value that equals the mean.

To calculate the Z-score for an observation, take the raw measurement, subtract the mean, and divide by the standard deviation. Mathematically, the formula for that process is the following:

$$Z = \frac{X - \mu}{\sigma}$$

The further away an observation's Z-score is from zero, the more unusual it is. A standard cut-off value for finding outliers are Z-scores of +/-3 or further from zero. The probability distribution below displays the distribution of Z-scores in a standard normal distribution. Z-scores beyond +/- 3 are so extreme you can barely see the shading under the curve.

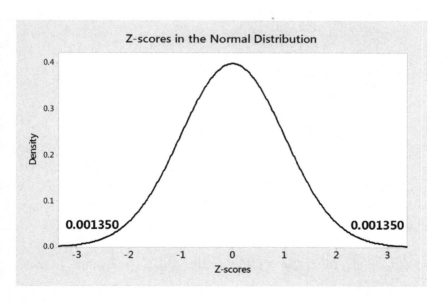

In a population that follows the normal distribution, Z-score values more extreme than +/- 3 have a probability of 0.0027 (2 * 0.00135), which is about 1 in 370 observations. However, if your data don't follow the normal distribution, this approach might not be accurate.

In our example dataset, I display the values in the example dataset along with the Z-scores. This approach identifies the same observation as being an outlier.

Height M	Z-score
1.5895	-0.34603
1.6508	-0.31975
1.7131	-0.29301
1.7136	-0.29283
1.7212	-0.28954
1.7296	-0.28595
1.7343	-0.28394
1.7663	-0.27020
1.8018	-0.25501
1.8394	-0.23888
1.8869	-0.21852
1.9357	-0.19757
1.9482	-0.19223
2.1038	-0.12551
10.8135	3.60910

Note that Z-scores can be misleading with small datasets because the maximum Z-score is limited to $(n-1) / \sqrt{n}$. (Shiffler, 1988) Indeed, our Z-score of ~3.6 is right near the maximum value for a sample size of 15. Sample sizes of 10 or fewer observations cannot have Z-scores that exceed a cutoff value of +/-3.

Also, note that the outlier's presence throws off the Z-scores because it inflates the mean and standard deviation as we saw earlier. Notice how all the Z-scores are negative except the outlier's value. If we calculated Z-scores without the outlier, they'd be different! Be aware that if your dataset contains outliers, Z-values are biased such that they appear to be less extreme (i.e., closer to zero).

Using the Interquartile Range to Create Outlier Fences

You can use the interquartile range (IQR), several quartile values, and an adjustment factor to calculate boundaries for what constitutes minor and major outliers. Minor and major denote the unusualness of the outlier relative to the overall distribution of values. Major outliers are more extreme. Analysts also refer to these categorizations as mild and extreme outliers.

The IQR is the middle 50% of the dataset. It's the range of values between the third quartile and the first quartile (Q3 – Q1). We can take the IQR, Q1, and Q3 values to calculate the following outlier fences for our dataset: lower outer, lower inner, upper inner, and upper outer. These fences determine whether data points are outliers and whether they are mild or extreme.

Values that fall inside the two inner fences are not outliers. Let's see how this method works using our example dataset.

Using statistical software, I can determine the interquartile range along with the Q1 and Q3 values for our example dataset. We'll need these values to calculate the "fences" for identifying minor and major outliers. The output indicates that our Q1 value is 1.714 and the Q3 value is 1.936. Our IQR is 1.936 – 1.714 = 0.222.

```
Descriptive Statistics: Height M

Variable      Q1     Q3     IQR
Height M    1.714  1.936   0.222
```

To calculate the outlier fences, do the following:

1. Take your IQR and multiply it by 1.5 and 3. We'll use these values to obtain the inner and outer fences. For our example, the IQR equals 0.222. Consequently, 0.222 * 1.5 = 0.333 and

0.222 * 3 = 0.666. We'll use 0.333 and 0.666 in the following steps.

2. Calculate the inner and outer lower fences. Take the Q1 value and subtract the two values from step 1. The two results are the lower inner and outer outlier fences. For our example, Q1 is 1.714. So, the lower inner fence = 1.714 − 0.333 = 1.381 and the lower outer fence = 1.714 − 0.666 = 1.048.

3. Calculate the inner and outer upper fences. Take the Q3 value and add the two values from step 1. The two results are the upper inner and upper outlier fences. For our example, Q3 is 1.936. So, the upper inner fence = 1.936 + 0.333 = 2.269 and the upper outer fence = 1.936 + 0.666 = 2.602.

For our example dataset, the values for these fences are 1.048, 1.381, 2.269, and 2.602. Almost all of our data should fall between the inner fences, which are 1.381 and 2.269. At this point, we look at our data values and determine whether any qualify as being major or minor outliers. 14 out of the 15 data points fall inside the inner fences—they are not outliers. The 15th data point falls outside the upper outer fence—it's a major or extreme outlier.

The IQR method is helpful because it uses percentiles, which do not depend on a specific distribution. Importantly, percentiles are relatively robust to the presence of outliers compared to the other quantitative methods.

Boxplots use the IQR method to determine the inner fences. Typically, I'll use boxplots rather than calculating the fences myself when I want to use this approach. Of the quantitative approaches in this post, this is my preferred method.

Finding Outliers with Hypothesis Tests

You can use hypothesis tests to find outliers. Many outlier tests exist, but I'll focus on one to illustrate how they work. In this post, I demonstrate Grubbs' test, which tests the following hypotheses:

- **Null**: All values in the sample were drawn from a single population that follows the same normal distribution.
- **Alternative**: One value in the sample was not drawn from the same normally distributed population as the other values.

If the p-value for this test is less than your significance level, you can reject the null and conclude that one of the values is an outlier. The analysis identifies the value in question.

Let's perform this hypothesis test using our sample dataset. Grubbs' test assumes your data are drawn from a normally distributed population, and it can detect only one outlier. If you suspect you have additional outliers, use a different test.

```
Outlier Test: Height M

Method

Null hypothesis          All values from same normal distribution
Alternative hypothesis   Smallest or largest value is an outlier
Significance level       α = 0.05

Grubbs' Test

Variable    N   Mean   StDev    Min     Max     G       P
Height M   15  2.397  2.332   1.589  10.814  3.61   0.000


Outlier

Variable   Row   Outlier
Height M    15   10.8135
```

Grubbs' outlier test produces a p-value of 0.000. Because it is less than our significance level, we can conclude that our dataset contains an outlier. The output indicates it is the high value we found before.

If you use Grubbs' test and find an outlier, don't remove that outlier and perform the analysis again. That process can cause you to remove values that are not outliers.

Challenges of Using Outlier Hypothesis Tests: Masking and Swamping

When performing an outlier test, you either need to choose a procedure based on the number of outliers or specify the number of outliers for a test. Grubbs' test checks for only one outlier. However, other methods, such as the Tietjen-Moore Test, require you to specify the number of outliers. That's hard to do correctly! After all, you're performing the test to find outliers! Masking and swamping are two problems that can occur when you specify the incorrect number of outliers in a dataset.

Masking occurs when you specify too few outliers. The additional outliers that exist can affect the test so that it detects no outliers. For example, if you specify one outlier when there are two, the test can miss both outliers.

Conversely, swamping occurs when you specify too many outliers. In this case, the test identifies too many data points as being outliers. For example, if you specify two outliers when there is only one, the test might find two outliers.

Because of these problems, I'm not a big fan of outlier tests. More on this in the next section!

My Philosophy about Finding Outliers

As you saw, there are many ways to identify outliers. My philosophy is that you must use your in-depth knowledge about all the variables when analyzing data. Part of this knowledge is knowing what values are typical, unusual, and impossible.

I find that when you have this in-depth knowledge, it's best to use the more straightforward, visual methods. At a glance, data points that are potential outliers will pop out under your knowledgeable gaze. Consequently, I'll often use boxplots, histograms, and good old-fashioned data sorting! These simple tools provide enough information for me to find unusual data points for further investigation.

Typically, I don't use Z-scores and hypothesis tests to find outliers because of their various complications. Using outlier tests can be challenging because they usually assume your data follow the normal distribution, and then there's masking and swamping. Additionally, the existence of outliers makes Z-scores less extreme.

It's ironic, but these methods for identifying outliers are sensitive to the presence of outliers! Fortunately, as long as researchers use a simple way to display unusual values, a knowledgeable analyst is likely to know which values need further investigation.

In my view, the formal statistical tests and calculations are overkill because they can't definitively identify outliers. Ultimately, analysts must investigate unusual values and use their expertise to determine whether they are legitimate data points. Statistical procedures don't know the subject matter or the data collection process and can't make the final determination. You should not include or exclude an observation using only the results of a hypothesis test or statistical measure.

After you identify unusual values, investigate them. Remember, you should not necessarily remove all outliers. Outliers can be very informative about the subject-area and data collection process. It's vital to understand how outliers occur and whether they might happen again as a normal part of the process or study area.

Statistical Analyses that Can Handle Outliers

What do you do when you can't legitimately remove outliers, but they violate the assumptions of your statistical analysis? You want to include them but don't want them to distort the results. Fortunately, there are various statistical analyses up to the task. Here are several options you can try.

Nonparametric hypothesis tests are robust to outliers. For these alternatives to the more common parametric tests, outliers won't necessarily violate their assumptions or distort their results.

Bootstrapping techniques use the sample data as they are and don't make assumptions about distributions.

These analyses allow you to capture the full variability of your dataset without violating assumptions and skewing results. Read more about them in chapter 14.

Review and Next Steps

In chapters 9 and 10, we looked at hypothesis tests that assess various properties of continuous data. These properties include the mean, standard deviation, correlation, and distribution of values. Additionally, you saw how outliers could severely distort the results for a set of continuous data. Analysts must look for outliers and determine whether they should remove them from the dataset.

Now, we'll move on to other types of data. These types don't have as many characteristics to test as continuous data. However, you can still learn from them.

First up, binary data!

CHAPTER 11

Binary Data and Testing Proportions

Let's switch gears and move away from continuous data.

Binary data can have only two values. If you can place an observation into only two categories, you have a binary variable.

Binary data are useful for calculating proportions or percentages, such as the proportion of defective products in a sample. You simply take the number of faulty products and divide by the sample size. Analysts can present proportions using decimals (e.g., 0.75) or percentages (75%).

Hypothesis tests that assess proportions require binary data and allow you to use sample data to make inferences about population proportions.

Suppose we are assessing the effectiveness of flu vaccinations and have two groups, the control group and treatment group. The binary data values are "infected" and "not infected." We can use a proportions test to compare the proportion of flu infections in each group and determine whether the population proportions are different. If the vaccination group has a significantly lower proportion of infections than the control group, the vaccine is effective. We'll come back to this example later in this chapter.

When discussing binary data in the context of hypothesis tests and the binomial distribution, statisticians frequently use the terms "events" and "trials."

Events: One of the two values for your binary data. In your statistical software, you set the value you want to be an event. Using either value produces consistent results. However, one value usually makes more sense than the other for a study.

Trials: The number of people or items that the researchers are testing in each group. In the vaccine studies, it's the number of human subjects.

Proportion = Events / Trials.

For example, in flu shot studies, scientists typically use infections as the events. We're hoping the vaccine reduces the proportion of infections. However, you could set the test up so that events are the uninfected. In that case, you'd hope that the vaccine increases the proportion of subjects who are not infected. Either way, the results and p-values will tell the same story.

In this chapter, I'll cover the 1 Proportion test and the 2 Proportions test, and then take a look at the binomial distribution.

For proportions tests, you can simply enter the number of events and the number of trials for each group in your statistical software. Consequently, there are no data files to download for these examples. You'll see these values in each example.

One-Sample Proportion Test

Use the one-sample proportion test to compare your sample proportion to a hypothesized value for the population. Typically, researchers use a value that is meaningful for their study. This value forms the null hypothesis for the test. The procedure also creates a confidence interval of likely values for the population standard deviation.

With a 1 Proportion test, you don't need to perform the hypothesis test. If you just want to understand the estimate's precision, assess the confidence interval to identify the range of likely values. That information can be valuable even when you don't have a reference or hypothesized value.

Suppose you receive parts from a supplier who guarantees that less than 3% of all parts they produce are defective. You can use the 1 Proportion test to assess this claim.

The 1-sample proportion test has the following hypotheses:

- **Null hypothesis:** The population proportion equals the hypothesized proportion.
- **Alternative hypothesis:** The population proportion does not equal the hypothesized proportion.

If the p-value is less than your significance level (e.g., 0.05), you can reject the null hypothesis. The difference between the sample proportion and the hypothesized proportion is statistically significant. Your sample provides strong enough evidence to conclude that the population proportion does not equal the hypothesized value.

Assumptions

For reliable 1-sample proportion test results, your data should satisfy the following assumptions:

- Random sample
- Binary data. There are only two possible outcomes per trial.

Each trial is independent

The outcome of one trial does not influence the outcome of another trial. For example, when you flip a coin, the result of one flip doesn't affect the next flip.

The proportion remains constant over time

In some cases, this assumption is true because of physical properties, such as flipping a coin. However, if there is a chance the probability can change over time, you can use the P chart (a control chart) to confirm this assumption. For example, the proportion of defective products that a process produces can change over time.

Example of the 1 Proportion Test

A beverage company is creating a drink that will directly compete with a similar drink from another company. The company's goal is for 70% of the population to prefer their drink over the competitor's beverage. The company sets up a blind taste test and randomly selects 100 participants. In the study, 80% of the tasters prefer the company's drink.

Analysts use the 1 Proportion test to determine whether the difference between the sample proportion of 0.80 and the target proportion of 0.70 is statistically significant.

Events	Trials
80	100

```
Test and CI for One Proportion

Test of p = 0.7 vs ≠ 0.7


                                                 Exact
Sample    X     N   Sample p        95% CI      P-Value
1        80   100   0.800000  (0.708157, 0.873344)   0.029
```

Because the p-value is less than 0.05, we can reject the null and con-clude that the population proportion does not equal 0.70. Our sample provides sufficient evidence to support the notion that the population proportion is greater than the target value.

The sample estimate of the proportion is 0.8. However, because the estimate comes from a sample, it is unlikely to exactly equal the pop-ulation proportion. The confidence interval indicates the proportion of the population that prefers the company's beverage is likely be-tween ~0.71 and 0.87. This confidence interval excludes the null hy-pothesis value of 0.70, which is consistent with the statistically significant p-value.

How the Proportion Test Works

Like t-tests and F-tests, proportion tests use a probability distribution based on the null hypothesis to calculate p-values. Proportion tests use the binomial distribution, which describes the likelihood of binary events over a set number of trials.

Let's create a binomial distribution for the 1-sample proportion test example. In that example, we had a target proportion of 0.7 for the null hypothesis. Remember, p-value calculations assume that the null hypothesis is correct. So, we'll create a binomial distribution based on the null hypothesis value of 0.7.

Our binomial distribution has an event probability of 0.7 and 100 trials (our number of subjects). Our sample proportion was 0.8, and we want to see where that fits in the binomial distribution to understand how unusual it is if the null is true. Next, we'll shade the tails as we did for the t-test and F-test. We're using the two-tailed version, so we'll shade both tails that same distance out.

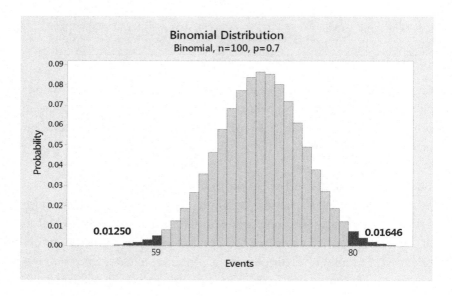

In this probability distribution plot, each bar represents the probability for a specific number of events. The peak bar is at 70 events because we're using a probability of 0.7 with 100 trials for the null hypothesis condition. As you move further away from 70 events, the probability declines. The 80 events we observed in our study is off in the right tail.

The left tail has a probability of 0.01250 and the right tail has a probability of 0.01646. The sum of these two probabilities equals 0.02896, which is the same p-value (with rounding) as the statistical output for the example. This graph shows that our sample proportion of 0.8 is unlikely to occur if the null hypothesis is correct.

Two-Sample Proportions Test

Use the two-sample proportions test to determine whether two population proportions are different and create a confidence interval of the difference between groups. This test uses independent samples. In other words, each group contains different people or items.

For example, use this test to determine whether two production methods produce different proportions of defective parts.

The hypotheses for the 2-sample proportions test are the following:

- **Null hypothesis:** The proportions for the two populations are equal.
- **Alternative hypothesis:** The proportions for the two populations are not equal.

If the p-value is less than your significance level (e.g., 0.05), you can reject the null hypothesis. The difference between the two proportions is statistically significant. Your sample provides strong enough evidence to conclude that the two population proportions are not equal.

Assumptions

For reliable 2-sample proportions test results, your data should satisfy the following assumptions:

- Random sample
- Binary data
- Independent groups
- Each trial is independent
- The proportions remain constant over time

Three Examples for the 2 Proportions Test

I'll present three examples of the two proportions test. The first example provides a quick overview of what you can learn from this test. The next two are a little more involved. One is a fun Mythbusters experiment that also teaches a valuable lesson about statistical power.

The last example is about a more serious topic—the effectiveness of flu vaccinations.

Quick Example 2 Proportions

For our first example, we will make a decision based on the proportions of defective parts. Our goal is to determine whether two methods produce different proportions of defective parts. We take a random sample of 130 parts from each production method. Events are defective parts. Let's analyze these proportions!

Sample	Events	Trials
1	8	130
2	19	130

```
Test and CI for Two Proportions

Sample    X    N   Sample p
1         8   130  0.061538
2        19   130  0.146154


Difference = p (1) - p (2)
Estimate for difference:   -0.0846154
95% CI for difference:   (-0.158060, -0.0111707)
Test for difference = 0 (vs ≠ 0):   Z = -2.26 P-Value = 0.024

Fisher's exact test: P-Value = 0.040
```

Both p-values are less than 0.05. The sample evidence is strong enough to reject the null hypothesis and conclude that Method 1 produces a smaller proportion of defects (~0.062) than Method 2 (~0.146). In this case, each population represents all future output using each method. We can conclude that Method 1 produces a lower proportion of defective parts.

Additionally, the confidence interval indicates that the range of likely values for the population difference between proportions is [-0.158 - 0.011]. These are negative values because it is calculating Method 1 – Method 2. The confidence interval excludes the value of zero (no difference between groups), so we can conclude that the population rates are different.

While the point estimate for the difference between proportions is -0.085, which seems important, the confidence interval almost includes zero (-0.011). While you can be reasonably sure that Method 1 produces fewer defects than Method 2, you are less confident that the difference is important in the real world.

Binomial Exact Test vs. Normal Approximation

In the two-sample proportions test, you might have noticed that there are two p-values. There is the exact test p-value and another p-value associated with a Z-score. You'll see that again in the upcoming examples.

The one- and two-sample proportions tests can use an exact test or a normal approximation. Each test produces its own p-value. The ability to use either method exists because the normal distribution can approximate the binomial distribution in some cases. For example, the probability plot on the next page displays a normal distribution that follows the binomial distribution closely.

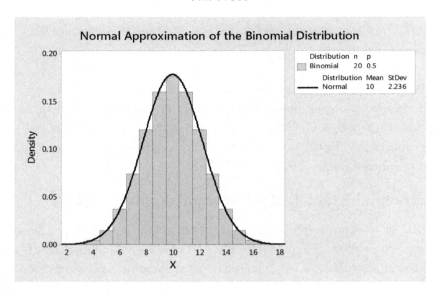

The exact test derives its p-value from the Binomial distribution itself, which is why it's an exact test. I showed you how that works in the 1-sample proportion test section. The p-value for the Z-score is based on the normal approximation.

Many statistics textbooks use the normal approximation method because it is easier for students to calculate manually. However, the exact test is more accurate.

Normal distributions can adequately approximate the binomial distribution when the event probability is near 0.5 or when the number of trials is large. The normal approximation uses n*p and the square root of n*p*(1-p) for its mean and standard deviation, respectively. Where:

- n = number of trials
- p = event probability

Mythbusters Example: Are Yawns Contagious?

When it comes to hypothesis testing, statistics help you avoid opinions about when an effect is large and how many samples you need to collect. Feelings about these things can be *way* off—even among those who regularly perform experiments and collect data! These hunches can lead you to incorrect conclusions. Always perform the correct hypothesis tests so you understand the strength of your evidence.

In my house, we're all big fans of the Mythbusters. This fun show tests whether different myths and urban legends could have really happened. Along the way, they perform experiments in a controlled and repeatable manner and collect data. This process involves lots of planning, custom equipment, reducing potential sources of variation, and many explosions. All good stuff. However, they're not always the best when it comes to statistical analysis and hypothesis testing.

Don't get me wrong. I think the Mythbusters are great because they make science fun and place a high value on using data to make decisions. It's a great way to bring science to life for kids! Unfortunately, they occasionally draw incorrect conclusions from their data because they don't use statistics.

One of the things I love about statistics is that hypothesis testing helps you objectively evaluate the evidence. You set the significance level before the study, analyze the data, and then decide using the p-value. You don't have to worry about a subjective assessment about whether an effect appears large enough while simultaneously trying to factor in the sample size and sample variability!

In this example, I'll detail their investigation into the myth that yawns are contagious and show how they would have benefited by using hypothesis testing and estimating an adequate sample size.

I think we've all heard that yawns are contagious. If you see someone yawn, it sure seems like you're more likely to yawn too. The

Mythbusters decided they were going to test this myth. They recruited 50 people under the pretense that they were looking for people to appear on the show.

The recruiter spoke to each subject one-on-one and intentionally either yawned or did not yawn during the session. After listening to the recruiter, the subjects sat in a small room for a fixed amount of time. The Mythbusters secretly observed the subjects and recorded whether they yawned.

The Mythbusters recorded these data:

- Recruiter did yawn (treatment group): 10 out of 34 (29%) of the subjects yawned.
- Recruiter did not yawn (control group): 4 out of 16 (25%) of the subjects yawned.

When it came time to determine the results of their experiment, Jamie Hyneman said that the data confirmed the myth. Yawns are contagious. He stated that the difference of 4% is significant thanks to the large sample size (n=50). Unfortunately, Jaime based this conclusion on intuition rather than a statistical test. I'm going to analyze this more meticulously to see if hypothesis testing agrees with Jamie!

The data contain proportions for two groups, so we'll use the two proportions test. There's no conceivable way that exposure to yawns will cause subjects in the treatment group to yawn less than the control group. Consequently, we'll use a one-tailed test to determine whether the treatment group has a higher proportion than the control group.

Sample	Events	Trials
Treatment	10	34
Control	4	16

The two proportions test produces the following results for the yawn data:

```
Test and CI for Two Proportions

Sample   X    N   Sample p
1       10   34   0.294118
2        4   16   0.250000


Difference = p (1) - p (2)
Estimate for difference:  0.0441176
95% lower bound for difference:  -0.175487
Test for difference = 0 (vs > 0):  Z = 0.33 P-Value = 0.371


* NOTE * The normal approximation may be inaccurate for small
samples.

Fisher's exact test: P-Value = 0.513
```

There are two P-values and we'll use the one for Fisher's exact test. This test is for small samples, and the note indicates that our sample is small. The P-value of 0.513 is well above any standard significance level.

We fail to reject the null hypothesis. The sample does **not** contain sufficient evidence to conclude that the subjects exposed to yawns tended to yawn more frequently. Additionally, the output indicates that the sample size is **small!** When working with binary data, you often need larger sample sizes than is typical for continuous data.

Unfortunately, Jamie was wrong about both the statistical significance and having a large sample size!

Assess Statistical Power to Estimate the Correct Sample Size

When the Mythbusters conclude that a myth isn't true, they often find the extreme conditions that can force the myth to occur. Usually, this involves an explosion. I'd love to include an explosion in this example, but I don't want to damage your device!

Instead, I'll produce a figurative bang by estimating how many subjects the Mythbusters should have recruited. I'll perform a power and sample size calculation to determine the sample size necessary for the test to have a decent chance of detecting an effect if one actually exists. Hint: The answer is bound to prompt Adam Savage's to wave his arms around in his characteristic manner!

In many fields, a good benchmark power value to aim for is 0.8. At this level, a hypothesis test has an 80% probability of detecting a difference if it exists.

The study estimated an effect of 0.04, which was not statistically significant. For the power analysis, I'm going to find the sample size that yields a statistical power of 0.8 for a difference of 0.10 (rather than 0.04) for a two proportions hypothesis test. After all, if the difference is 0.04, that's so tiny that it's not practically significant in the real world even if a study found it to be statistically significant. I'll calculate power using a one-tailed test.

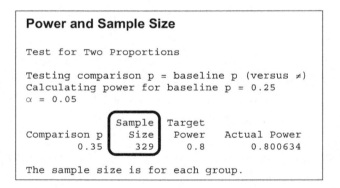

If the actual population difference between the groups is 10 percentage points (25% vs. 35%), the Mythbusters need to recruit 329 subjects per group (648 total)! Well, they were only off by 600!

The sample size is so large because the effect size is small and hypothesis tests for binary data require larger samples than tests for continuous data.

The Mythbusters Need Statistics and Hypothesis Testing!

Using the two proportions hypothesis test and power calculation, we learned a couple of things:

- The sample data do not support the hypothesis that yawns are contagious.
- The sample size was too small to provide adequate statistical power.

I have a lot of research experience working in labs at a university. Based on this experience, I don't see the Mythbusters experiment as a failure at all. Instead, I see it as a pilot study. For an experiment, you often need to conduct a small pilot study to work the kinks out and develop the initial estimates. It helps you avoid costly mistakes by not going straight to a large-scale experiment where things might not go as planned.

That's how the scientific method works. You state the hypothesis, design and set up the controlled conditions for an experiment, and then evaluate the data with a hypothesis test. You assess those results and, if necessary, make adjustments to improve the next study.

If this study occurred in the research arena, the researchers would ask themselves whether it's worth conducting additional research on the subject. Are the potential benefits worth the costs? In this case, the benefits of learning whether yawns are contagious are small compared to the costs associated with a study of 650 subjects. It's probably not going to happen!

Even though the results of this study are not statistically significant, we still learned something important!

We are still big fans of the Mythbusters! This study just reconfirms that science, research, and statistical analysis are tricky. Sometimes your intuition can lead you astray. Statistics can help keep you grounded by providing an objective assessment of your data with hypothesis testing. After all, the Mythbusters went to a lot of effort to collect their data. They ought to know what the data are really telling them!

2 Proportions Example: Flu Shot Effectiveness

Flu season arrives every Fall.

Do you debate getting a flu shot every year? I get flu shots every year. I realize that they're not perfect, but I figure they're a low-cost way to reduce my chances of a crummy week suffering from the flu.

The media report that flu shots have an effectiveness of approximately 68%. But what does that mean exactly?

In this example, I explore the effectiveness of flu shots from a statistical viewpoint. We'll statistically analyze the data ourselves to go beyond the simplified accounts that the media presents.

My background is in scientific research. And, I love numbers—they're how I understand the world. Whenever I want to understand a topic, I combine these two things—numbers and scientific research.

To understand flu shot effectiveness, we'll look at scientific, peer-reviewed articles. By assessing their methodology, seeing the actual data, and how they draw their conclusions, we'll be able to comprehend flu shot effectiveness at a much deeper level.

We're going to evaluate only double-blind, randomized controlled trials (RCTs), the gold standard. RCTs are more expensive to conduct than observational studies, but they provide the tremendous benefit of identifying causal relationships rather than mere correlation. After all, we need to determine whether flu shots *cause* a reduction in the risk of contracting the flu.

I've found two influenza vaccination RCTs for us to analyze. The CDC list these studies on their website in a reference section for healthcare professionals. We'll take a close look at these studies and analyze their data ourselves!

Defining the Effectiveness of Flu Shots

The definition of influenza vaccine effectiveness is very precise in studies. It's essential to understand the meaning and its context before we continue.

Flu shots contain vaccines for three or four strains of the influenza virus that scientists predict will be the most common strains in a flu season. However, there are many other viruses (other strains of flu and non-flu) that can make you sick. Some of these are flu-*like* illnesses that are not the flu but can make you feel like you have the flu.

Consequently, the best flu vaccination studies use a lab to identify the specific virus that makes their subjects sick. These studies count participants as being infected with the flu only when he or she catches one of the influenza strains in the vaccine. Flu shot effectiveness is the reduction in cases involving these particular strains among those who were vaccinated compared to those who were not.

Two Flu Vaccination Studies

Let's get to the data! This is the exciting part where the rubber meets the road. The media discusses the effectiveness, but it all stems from these counts of sick people in experimental groups. These deceptively simple looking tables contain the answers to our questions. They're deceptively simple because these studies use meticulous experimental methodologies, time consuming data collection and validation procedures, and extensive subject selection protocols to collect these data.

The Beran Study

Beran et al. study the 2006/2007 flu season and follows its participants from September to May. Participants in this study range from 18-64 years old. The table indicates the number of lab-confirmed flu cases for the treatment and control groups. (Beran, et al., 2009)

Treatment	Flu count (Events)	Group size (Trials)
Vaccine	49	5103
Placebo	74	2549

This table represents observations from a random sample of the population. To determine whether the observed difference between the group proportions represents an effect in the population, we need to perform a hypothesis test. In the case, we'll use the 2 Proportions test.

This test answers the question: Is the difference between the proportion of sick people in each group statistically significant?

```
Test and CI for Two Proportions

Sample    X      N   Sample p
1        49   5103   0.009602
2        74   2549   0.029031


Difference = p (1) - p (2)
Estimate for difference:  -0.0194288
95% CI for difference:    (-0.0264744, -0.0123832)
Test for difference = 0 (vs not = 0):  Z = -5.40   P-Value = 0.000

Fisher's exact test: P-Value = 0.000
```

The p-value of 0.000 indicates that the difference between the two groups is statistically significant. The Sample p column displays the proportion of flu cases in each group, which I'll convert to percentages (0.96% vs. 2.9%). The estimate for the difference shows that the vaccinated group has 1.9% fewer cases than the placebo group. The confidence interval indicates that we can be 95% confident that the population difference is between 2.65% and 1.24%.

Because this study is an RCT, it's reasonable to assume that the vaccinations cause the reduction.

The difference between the groups (1.9%) is not what we hear about in the media. They report the vaccine effectiveness, which is the relative reduction in the risk for the vaccinated group. The formula for effectiveness is:

$$1 - \frac{\text{Vaccinated Flu Cases Proportion}}{\text{Unvaccinated Flu Cases Proportion}}$$

$$1 - \frac{0.009602}{0.029031} = 0.669$$

This study reports a 66.9% vaccination effectiveness for the flu shot compared to the control group.

The Monto Study

The Monto et al. study evaluates the 2007-2008 flu season and follows its participants from January to April. Participants are 18-49 years old. (Monto, et al., 2009)

Treatment	Flu count	Group size
Vaccine	28	813
Placebo	35	325

Let's perform the 2 Proportions test on these data.

Test and CI for Two Proportions

```
Sample   X    N   Sample p
1       28   813  0.034440
2       35   325  0.107692


Difference = p (1) - p (2)
Estimate for difference:   -0.0732520
95% CI for difference:   (-0.109210, -0.0372943)
Test for difference = 0 (vs not = 0):   Z = -3.99   P-Value = 0.000

Fisher's exact test: P-Value = 0.000
```

Like before, the small p-value indicates that the difference between the flu shot group and the placebo group is statistically significant. For this study, the vaccinated group has 7.3% fewer cases of the flu. Let's calculate the effectiveness:

$$1 - \frac{0.034440}{0.107692} = 0.680$$

This study finds a 68.0% vaccine effectiveness for the flu shot.

Flu Shot Conclusions

First, isn't it cool how we can analyze their data and draw our own conclusions? Our findings are consistent with those reported by the news media. The flu vaccine produces a statistically significant reduction in the number of influenza infections. Further, the flu shots are about 68% effective.

However, seeing the data for yourself, did you gain some new insights? I know I did. I think the percentage point reduction in flu cases sounds less impressive than the 68% effectiveness. The former measures absolute risk while the later measures relative risk. Same data but different ways of presenting the results.

Because these studies used inferential procedures (random sampling), sound experimental methodology (random assignment, lab tests, etc.), and hypothesis tests to analyze the data, we can reasonably generalize the results beyond the sample to the population and account for random sampling error.

Scientifically speaking, it would have been unhelpful only knowing that the vaccine was effective for just this group of subjects. However, knowing that it is effective for the population *is* valuable!

Distributions for Binary Data

You saw how continuous data can fit different probability distributions. Binary data also follows one of several distributions. However, there is a vital difference between continuous distributions and binary distributions. While you test continuous data to determine which distribution your data follow, you don't check your binary data in the same manner.

Instead, if you want to use a probability distribution for binary data to model your subject area, you need to determine whether your data satisfy the assumptions instead of performing a goodness-of-fit test. If you are confident that your binary data meet the assumptions, you're good to go!

Because you don't use hypothesis tests for binary distributions, I'll just summarize the binomial distribution here, which is the most common distribution that analysts use for binary data. However, in my *Introduction to Statistics* book, I cover four probability distributions for binary data in detail.

Use the binomial distribution to model the number of times an event occurs within a constant number of trials.

The binomial distribution has the following four assumptions:

1. **There are only two possible outcomes per trial.** For example, yes or no, pass or fail, etc.
2. **Each trial is independent.** The outcome of one trial does not influence the outcome of another trial. For example, when you flip a coin, the result of one flip doesn't affect the next flip.
3. **The probability remains constant over time.** In some cases, this assumption is true based on the physical properties, such as flipping a coin. However, if there is a chance the probability can change over time, you can use the P chart (a control chart) to confirm this assumption. For example, it's possible that the probability that a process produces defective products can change over time.
4. **The number of trials is fixed.** The binomial distribution models the frequency of events over a set number of trials. If you need to model a different characteristic, use a different distribution.

Typically, you must have good knowledge about the process, data collection methodology, and your goals to determine whether you should use the binomial distribution. If you can meet all four of these assumptions, you can use the binomial distribution.

Example of the Binomial Distribution

For the binomial distribution, you input the event probability and the number of trials. For this example, I use an event probability of 1.5% for a defective product occurring and a sample size of 30.

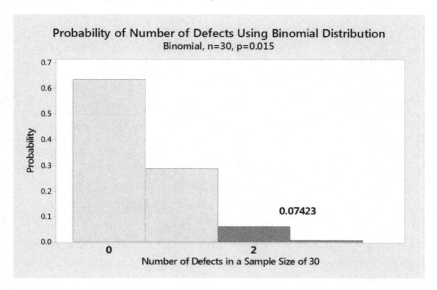

The individual bars indicate the proportion of samples that will have the specified number of defective products. For example, the leftmost bar in the graph shows you'd expect just over 60% of the samples to have zero faulty products. Additionally, the darker shaded bars sum the probabilities for having at least two defective products. The binomial distribution predicts that about 7.4% of the samples will have two or more defective products.

Other distributions that use binary data

Several other probability distributions use binary data. I list them in the next table, along with how they differ from the binomial distribution. Each distribution has assumptions or goals that vary a bit from the binomial distribution.

Distribution	Main differentiation from the binomial distribution
Negative binomial	Models the number of trials to produce a fixed number of events.
Geometric	Models the number of trials to produce the first event.
Hypergeometric	Assumes that you are drawing samples from a small population with no replacements, which causes the probabilities to change.

If you are working with binary variables, the choice of binary distribution depends on the population, constancy of the probability, and your goals. When you confirm the assumptions, there typically is no need to perform a goodness-of-fit test.

Review and Next Steps

Throughout this chapter, we looked at binary data and what we can learn from it. We mainly focused on one- and two-sample proportions tests. These tests answer questions about the proportion of events in one or two populations.

1-Sample: Was your sample drawn from a population with a different proportion of events than the hypothesized value?

2-Sample: Were your samples drawn from populations that have different proportions of events?

Along the way, you learned that proportions tests can require notably larger sample sizes than tests for continuous data.

Then we took a quick look at the binomial distribution. You don't use a hypothesis test to determine whether your data fit the binomial distribution. Instead, you check the assumptions.

In the next chapter, we'll look at count data and Poisson distribution.

CHAPTER 12

Count Data and Rates of Occurrence

In statistics, count data represent the number of events or character-istics over a given length of time, area, volume, etc. For example, you can count the number of cigarettes smoked per day, meteors seen per hour, or the occurrence of a particular crime in a geographic region.

Count data have different characteristics than continuous data. These differences make using hypothesis tests designed for continuous data (e.g., t-tests) potentially problematic. Count data are discrete values and contain non-negative integers (0, 1, 2, 4, etc.). Additionally, many distributions of count data have skewed distributions. If only we had a special probability distribution designed for this type of data . . . cue the Poisson distribution!

The Poisson distribution plot on the next page reflects a study area that averages 2.24 counts during the observation period. You can see the distribution itself consists of discrete counts and is right-skewed. We'll use data that follow this distribution for two examples in this chapter.

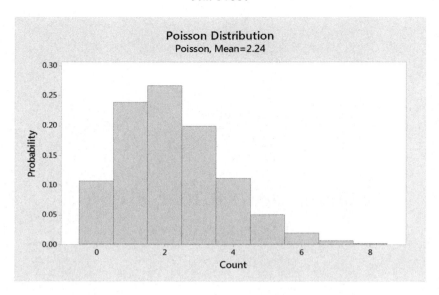

The Poisson distribution is a discrete probability distribution that models the count of events or characteristics over a constant observation space, such as a particular length of time, area, volume, and so on. Values must be integers that are greater than or equal to zero.

Hypothesis tests that use the Poisson distribution can assess count data. Additionally, you can use this distribution to make predictions. The Poisson distribution is defined by a single parameter lambda (λ), which is the mean number of occurrences during the specified interval.

The Poisson hypothesis tests that you'll learn about in this chapter assess the mean number of occurrences of an event in the observation unit you define.

While the Rate Tests use the Poisson distribution to calculate p-values, the method is more complex than t-tests, F-tests, and proportion tests. Unfortunately, I won't be able to show you how they work using graphs as I've done with the other tests.

Analyze the CSV data file that contains datasets for both the one-sample and two-sample Poisson Rate tests: CountDataExamples.

One-Sample Poisson Rate Test

Use the one-sample Poisson rate test to compare your sample occurrence rate to a hypothesized value for the population. Typically, researchers use a value that is meaningful for their study. This value forms the null hypothesis for the test. The procedure also creates a confidence interval of likely values for the population rate of occurrence.

With a 1-sample Poisson rate test, you don't need to perform the hypothesis test. If you just want to understand the estimate's precision, assess the confidence interval to identify the range of likely values. That information can be valuable even when you don't have a reference or hypothesized value.

For example, a safety inspector might compare the accident rate at a nursing home to a standard rate of occurrence to determine whether a construction project needs to improve the intersection.

The 1-sample Poisson rate test has the following hypotheses:

- **Null hypothesis:** The population rate equals the hypothesized rate.
- **Alternative hypothesis:** The population rate does not equal the hypothesized rate.

If the p-value is less than your significance level (e.g., 0.05), you can reject the null hypothesis. The difference between the sample rate and the hypothesized rate is statistically significant. Your sample provides strong enough evidence to conclude that the population rate does not equal the hypothesized value.

Assumptions

For reliable 1-sample Poisson rate test results, your data should satisfy the following assumptions:

- Random sample
- Data must be counts per a fixed observation unit
- Each trial is independent. The count for one observation unit doesn't affect the count for the next unit.
- Counts follow the Poisson distribution.

Example of the 1-Sample Poisson Rate Test

Suppose a safety inspector needs to monitor the number of falls per month at a large nursing home. The inspector randomly selects 50 days to observe. He enters the number of daily accidents in a worksheet like this:

Falls
2
0
2
2
4

Each value denotes the count of falls in one day. The dataset has 50 values that cover 50 days.

The inspector needs to compare the mean sample rate of occurrence (2.24) to a reference value of 1.75. If the mean rate exceeds this value, the nursing home must implement corrective measures.

Test and CI for One-Sample Poisson Rate: Falls

```
Test of rate = 1.75 vs ≠ 1.75


                  Total           Rate of                              Exact
Variable    Occurrences    N    Occurrence       95% CI               P-Value
Falls               112   50      2.24000   (1.84441, 2.69530)         0.014


"Length" of observation = 1.
```

The p-value is less than 0.05. Consequently, we reject the null hypothesis that the nursing home's accident rate equals the target value. We can conclude that the nursing home's daily rate of falls (2.24) exceeds the reference rate of 1.75 falls per day.

Additionally, the confidence interval estimates the population's rate of falls is likely to be between 1.84 and 2.70 per day. This range excludes the reference value of 1.75, which is why the result is statistically significant. The inspector will need to write up a report about the nursing home.

Two-Sample Poisson Rate Test

Use the two-sample Poisson rate test to determine whether two population rates are different and create a confidence interval of the difference between groups. This test uses independent samples. In other words, each group contains different people or items.

For example, use this test to determine whether two production methods produce different proportions of defective parts.

The hypotheses for the 2-sample Poisson rate test are the following:

- **Null hypothesis:** The rates for the two populations are equal.
- **Alternative hypothesis:** The rates for the two populations are not equal.

If the p-value is less than your significance level (e.g., 0.05), you can reject the null hypothesis. The difference between the two rates is statistically significant. Your sample provides strong enough evidence to conclude that the two population rates are not equal.

Assumptions

For reliable 2-sample Poisson rate test results, your data should satisfy the following assumptions:

- Random sample
- Data must be counts per a fixed unit
- Each trial is independent. The count for one observation unit doesn't affect the count for the next unit.
- Independent groups. Different items or people in each group.
- Counts follow the Poisson distribution.

Example of the Two-Sample Poisson Rate Test

Suppose an analyst wants to compare the number of customer complaints at two store locations. The analyst counts the number of complaints during a business day for a random sample of 30 days.

The analyst enters the number of complaints in a worksheet like this:

Store 1	Store 2
1	1
7	10
3	4
4	2
4	0
6	4

Each cell represents the number of complaints in a day and there are 30 days for each store.

Let's run the test!

```
Test and CI for Two-Sample Poisson Rates: Store 1, Store 2

                  Total           Rate of
Variable     Occurrences   N     Occurrence
Store 1            107 30          3.56667
Store 2            161 30          5.36667


Difference = rate(Store 1) - rate(Store 2)
Estimate for difference: -1.8
95% CI for difference: (-2.86953, -0.730467)
Test for difference = 0 (vs ≠ 0): Z = -3.30 P-Value = 0.001

Fisher's exact test: P-Value = 0.001
```

The exact test p-value is less than 0.05. Consequently, we can reject the null hypothesis that the two population rates are equal.

The output indicates that the difference between the rate of complaints per day for Store 1 (3.56667) and Store 2 (5.36667) is statistically significant. We can conclude that Store 1 receives customer complaints at a lower rate than Store 2.

Furthermore, the confidence interval estimates that the population difference between these two stores is between -2.87 and -0.73. The negative values reflect the fact that Store 1 has a lower rate than Store 2 (i.e., Store 1 – Store 2 < 0). The confidence interval excludes the value of zero (no difference between groups), so we can conclude that the population rates are different.

Poisson Exact Test vs. Normal Approximation

In the two-sample Poisson rate test, you might have noticed that there are two p-values. There is the exact test p-value and another p-value associated with a Z-score.

The one- and two-sample Poison rate tests can use an exact test or a normal approximation. Each test produces its own p-value. The ability to use either method exists because the normal distribution can approximate the Poisson distribution in some cases. For example, the probability plot below shows a normal distribution that follows the Poisson distribution closely.

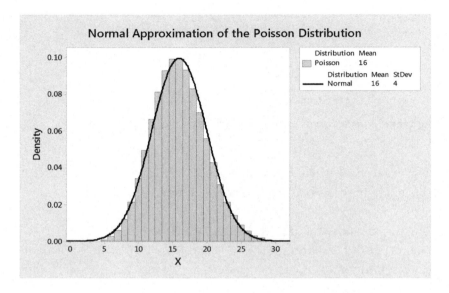

The exact test derives its p-value from the Poisson distribution itself, which is why it's an exact test. The p-value for the Z-score is based on the normal approximation.

Many statistics textbooks use the normal approximation method because it is easier for students to calculate manually. However, the exact test is more accurate.

Normal distributions can adequately approximate the Poisson distribution when the Poisson mean (λ) is 10 or more. The normal approximation uses the Poisson mean and the square root of the Poisson mean for its mean and standard deviation, respectively.

Goodness-of-Fit for a Poisson Distribution

You can often use the Poisson distribution to model count data. However, not all count data fit the Poisson distribution. This situation is similar to how many continuous variables follow the normal distribution, but not all of them. Fortunately, the Goodness-of-Fit Test for the Poisson distribution can help you determine whether the Poisson distribution is right for your data.

The Poisson distribution has only one parameter, which is the mean rate of occurrence. However, the distribution assumes that the variance of the distribution equals the mean—and that's not always true.

If you are working with count data and categorical data, chances are you'll need to perform a Chi-square goodness-of-fit test to decide if your data fit a particular discrete probability distribution. These tests compare the theoretical frequencies to the frequencies of the observed values. If the difference is statistically significant, you can conclude that your data do not follow that specific discrete distribution.

Like any hypothesis test, the Chi-square goodness-of-fit for the Poisson distribution has a null hypothesis and an alternative hypothesis.

- H_0: The sample data follow the Poisson distribution.
- H_1: The sample data do not follow the Poisson distribution.

For goodness-of-fit tests, small p-values indicate that you can reject the null hypothesis and conclude that your data were not drawn from a population with the specified distribution. Consequently, goodness-of-fit tests are a rare case where you look for high p-values to identify candidate distributions.

For now, I'll show you how to test whether your discrete data follow the Poisson distribution. In the next chapter, you'll learn how to use it with categorical variables. Analyze the CSV file that contains the data for both examples: DiscreteGOF.

I'll use the nursing home falls dataset to show you how to determine whether your data follow the Poisson distribution.

To determine whether these data follow the Poisson distribution, we need to use the Chi-Squared Goodness-of-Fit Test for the Poisson distribution. The statistical output for this test is below.

Goodness-of-Fit Test for Poisson Distribution

Data column: Accidents

Poisson mean for Accidents = 2.24

Accidents	Observed	Poisson Probability	Expected	Contribution to Chi-Sq
0	7	0.106459	5.3229	0.52839
1	8	0.238467	11.9234	1.29097
2	13	0.267083	13.3542	0.00939
3	10	0.199422	9.9711	0.00008
>=4	12	0.188569	9.4285	0.70136

N	N*	DF	Chi-Sq	P-Value
50	0	3	2.53020	0.470

This test compares the observed counts to the expected counts, which you can see in the output. The procedure derives the expected counts using the Poisson distribution. If you compare the Poisson Probability column to the Poisson probability plot at the beginning of this chapter, you'll notice that the numeric values correspond to each bar's probabilities in the graph. That graph displays a Poisson distribution with a mean of 2.24, which is the same as our nursing home data.

When we look at the chi-square test of independence in the next chapter, I'll show you in detail how chi-square tests assess the differences between observed and expected counts to determine statistical significance. For now, let's interpret the output.

The p-value is larger than the common significance level of 0.05. Consequently, the test result suggests that these data follow the Poisson distribution. You can use the Poisson distribution to make predictions about the probabilities associated with different counts. You can also use analyses that assume the data follow the Poisson distribution.

These analyses include the 1- and 2-sample Poisson rate analyses, the U Chart, and Poisson regression.

Review and Next Steps

In this chapter, we looked at the unique challenges that count data create. Count data form distributions of discrete values that are non-negative integers and are often skewed. Fortunately, the Poisson distribution can often model this type of data.

Using hypothesis tests that incorporate the Poisson distribution, we can use sample estimates for rates of occurrences to draw conclusions about population rates of occurrences.

Finally, just as continuous data do not always follow the normal distribution, count data do not always follow the Poisson distribution. We finished the chapter by looking at the Goodness-of-Fit Test for Poisson distributions, which helps you determine whether your count data fit the Poisson distribution.

Next up, categorical variables! We'll use the chi-square test from this chapter in two new ways for categorical data.

CHAPTER 13

Categorical Variables

Categorical data have values that you can put into a countable number of distinct groups based on a characteristic. For a categorical variable, you can assign categories, but the categories have no natural order. Analysts also refer to categorical data as both attribute and nominal variables.

For example, type of damage is a categorical variable with values such as scratch, dent, and tear.

In previous chapters, we saw how categorical variables can define the groups for analyses that compare groups by means, variability, proportions, and rate of occurrence. However, sometimes you want to analyze the categorical variables themselves rather than using them to define groups.

In this chapter, you'll learn how to analyze two properties of categorical variables, association and distribution of values.

Chi-Square Test of Independence

The Chi-square test of independence determines whether there is a statistically significant relationship between categorical variables. It is a hypothesis test that answers the question—do the values of one categorical variable depend on the value of other categorical variables? It is similar to the correlation between two continuous variables.

As you no doubt guessed, I'm a huge fan of statistics. I'm also a big Star Trek fan. Consequently, I'm thrilled to be writing about both in this example! In the *Star Trek* TV series, Captain Kirk and the crew wear different colored uniforms to identify the crewmember's work area. Those who wear red shirts have the unfortunate reputation of dying more often than those who wear gold or blue shirts.

I'll show you how the Chi-square test of independence works. Then, I'll show you how to perform the analysis and interpret the results by working through the example. I'll use this test to determine whether wearing the dreaded red shirt in Star Trek is the kiss of death!

The Chi-square test of association evaluates relationships between categorical variables. Like all hypothesis tests, the Chi-square test has both a null hypothesis and an alternative hypothesis.

The two hypotheses for the chi-square test of independence are the following:

- **Null**: The variables are independent. No relationship exists.
- **Alternative**: A relationship between the variables exists. Knowing the value of one variable *does* help you predict the value of the other variable.

The Chi-square test of independence works by comparing the distribution that you observe to the distribution that you expect if there is no relationship between the categorical variables. In the Chi-square context, the word "expected" is equivalent to what you'd expect if the null hypothesis is true. If your observed distribution is sufficiently different from the expected distribution (no relationship), you can reject the null hypothesis and infer that the variables are related.

In the previous chapter, we used a different form of the chi-squared test to determine whether our sample data were drawn from a population that follows the Poisson distribution. In that example, the expected values were the distribution of counts predicted by the Poisson distribution. That test determined whether our sample counts differed from the Poisson distribution. Now, we've changed the test so the expected values are the counts of observations that we'd expect to see if there is no relationship between the categorical variables. You'll see yet another form of the chi-squared test later in this chapter when we test the distribution of categorical values.

Given that we're using the same test in different ways, I'll focus a little more on how it works. I'll use the same graphical approach as I do for t-tests and F-tests. You'll learn how these chi-square tests compare observed values to expected values and determine statistical significance. By changing the variety of expected values, it changes the nature of the test. That's how this test can also test for the Poisson distribution and test the distribution of categorical values.

For a Chi-square test, a p-value that is less than or equal to your significance level indicates there is sufficient evidence to conclude that the observed distribution is not the same as the expected distribution. For the test of independence, a significant p-value indicates you can conclude that a relationship exists between the categorical variables.

Star Trek Fatalities by Uniform Colors

We'll perform a Chi-square test of independence to determine whether there is a statistically significant association between shirt color and deaths. We need to use this test because these variables are both categorical variables. Shirt color can be only blue, gold, or red. Fatalities can be only dead or alive.

The color of the uniform represents each crewmember's work area. We will statistically assess whether there is a connection between uniform color and the fatality rate. Believe it or not, there are "real" data about the crew from authoritative sources and the show portrayed the deaths onscreen. The table indicates how many crewmembers are in each area and how many have died.

Color	Areas	Crew	Fatalities
Blue	Science and Medical	136	7
Gold	Command and Helm	55	9
Red	Operations, Engineering, and Security	239	24
Ship's total	All	430	40

For our example, we will determine whether the observed counts of deaths by uniform color are different from the distribution that we'd expect if there is no association between the two variables.

Analysts often use the Chi-square test of independence to assess potential relationships in a contingency table.

For the Star Trek example, uniform color and status are the two categorical variables. The contingency table below shows the combination of variable values, frequencies, and percentages.

	Blue	Gold	Red	Row total
Dead	7	9	24	40
Alive	129	46	215	390
Column total	136	55	239	N = 430
Column percentage (Dead)	5.15%	16.36%	10.04%	

If uniform color and fatality rates are independent, we'd expect the column percentage in the bottom row to be roughly equal for all uniform colors. After all, if there is no connection between these variables, there's no reason for the fatality rates to be different.

However, our fatality rates are not equal. Gold has the highest fatality rate at 16.36%, while Blue has the lowest at 5.15%. Red is in the middle at 10.04%. Does this inequality in our sample suggest that the fatality rates are different in the population? Does a relationship exist between uniform color and fatalities?

Thanks to random sampling error, our sample's fatality rates don't exactly equal the population's rates. If the population rates are equal, we'd likely still see differences in our sample. So, the question becomes, after factoring in sampling error, are the fatality rates in our sample different enough to conclude that they're different in the population? In other words, we want to be confident that the observed differences represent a relationship in the population rather than merely random fluctuations in the sample. That's where the chi-squared test for independence comes in!

To try it yourself, assess the CSV dataset: StarTrekFatalities.

You can use the dataset to perform the analysis in your preferred statistical software. The following are the Chi-squared test of independence results.

Tabulated statistics: Uniform Color, Status

```
Using frequencies in Frequency

Rows: Uniform Color    Columns: Status

            Alive     Dead       All

Blue          129        7        136
            94.85     5.15     100.00      Count < Expected
           123.35    12.65     136.00
           0.2589   2.5243         *

Gold           46        9         55
            83.64    14.36     100.00      Count > Expected
            49.88     5.12      55.00
           0.3024   2.9481         *

Red           215       24        239
            89.96    10.04     100.00      Count = Expected
           216.77    22.23     239.00
           0.0144   0.1405         *

All           390       40        430
            90.70     9.30     100.00
           390.00    40.00     430.00
               *        *          *

Cell Contents:          Count
                        % of Row
                        Expected count
                        Contribution to Chi-square


Pearson Chi-Square = 6.189, DF = 2, P-Value = 0.045
Likelihood Ratio Chi-Square = 6.132  DF = 2, P-Value = 0.047
```

In our statistical results, both p-values are less than 0.05. We can reject the null hypothesis and conclude there is a relationship between shirt color and deaths. The next step is to define that relationship.

Describing the relationship between categorical variables involves comparing the observed count to the expected count in each cell of the Dead column. I've annotated this comparison in the statistical output above. Additionally, you can graph each cell's contribution to the Chi-square statistic.

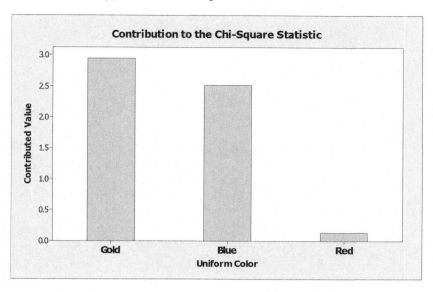

Surprise! It's the blue and gold uniforms that contribute the most to the Chi-square statistic and produce the statistical significance! Red shirts add almost nothing. In the statistical output, the comparison of observed counts to expected counts shows that blue shirts die less frequently than expected, gold shirts die more often than expected, and red shirts die at the expected rate.

The next graph reiterates these conclusions by displaying fatality percentages by uniform color along with the overall death rate.

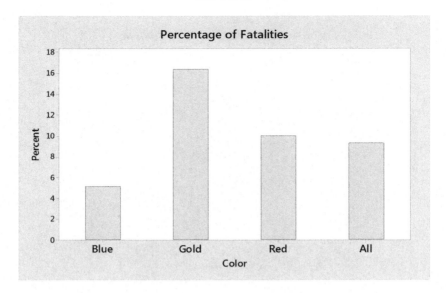

The Chi-square test indicates that red shirts don't die more frequently than expected. Hold on. There's more to this story! Later in this chapter, there is a bonus analysis that explains what is happening.

So far, we've looked at what this test of test independence analyzes and how to interpret the results. Now, let's dig deeper and see how it works.

How the Chi-square Test Works

The chi-square test of independence compares our sample data in the contingency table to the distribution of values we'd expect if the null hypothesis is correct. Let's construct the contingency table for a true null hypothesis.

For chi-squared tests, the term "expected frequencies" refers to the values we'd expect to see if the null hypothesis is correct. To calculate the expected frequency for a specific combination of categorical variables (e.g., blue shirts who died), multiply the column total (Blue) by the row total (Dead), and divide by the sample size.

Row total X Column total / Sample Size = Expected value for one table cell

To calculate the expected frequency for the Dead/Blue cell in our dataset, do the following:

- Find the row total for Dead (40)
- Find the column total for Blue (136)
- Multiply those two values and divide by the sample size (430)

40 * 136 / 430 = 12.65

If the null hypothesis is true, we'd expect to see 12.65 fatalities for wearers of the Blue uniforms in our sample. Of course, we can't have a fraction of a death, but that doesn't affect the results.

Please note that rounding errors cause the slight differences between the chi-square value and p-value in the previous sections and the upcoming sections.

Contingency Table with Expected Values

I'll calculate the expected values for all six cells representing the combinations of the three uniform colors and two statuses. I'll also include the observed values in our sample. Expected values are in parentheses.

	Blue	Gold	Red	Row total
Dead	7 (12.65)	9 (5.12)	24 (22.23)	40
Alive	129 (123.35)	46 (49.88)	215 (216.77)	390
Column% (Expected Dead)	9.3%	9.3%	9.3%	

In this table, notice how the column percentages for the expected dead are all 9.3%. This equality occurs when the null hypothesis is valid, which is the condition that the expected values represent.

Using this table, we can also compare the values we observe in our sample to the frequencies we'd expect if the null hypothesis that the variables are not related is correct.

For example, the observed frequency for Blue/Dead is less than the expected value (7 < 12.65). In our sample, deaths of those in blue uniforms occurred less frequently than expected if the variables are independent. On the other hand, the observed frequency for Gold/Dead is higher than the expected value (9 > 5.12). Meanwhile, the observed frequency for Red/Dead approximately equals the expected value. This interpretation matches what we concluded by assessing the column percentages in the first contingency table.

The chi-squared test works by mathematically comparing observed frequencies to the expected values, and boiling all those differences down into one number. Let's see how it does that!

Calculating the Chi-Squared Statistic

Most hypothesis tests calculate a test statistic. For example, t-tests use t-values and F-tests use F-values as their test statistics. These statistical tests compare your observed sample data to what you would expect if the null hypothesis is true. The calculations reduce your sample data down to one value representing how different your data are from the null.

For chi-squared tests, the test statistic is, unsurprisingly, chi-squared, or χ^2.

The chi-squared calculations involve a familiar concept in statistics—the sum of the squared differences between the observed and expected values. This concept is similar to how regression models assess goodness-of-fit using the sum of the squared differences.

Here's the formula for chi-squared.

$$\chi^2 = \sum \frac{(O - E)^2}{E}$$

Let's walk through it!

To calculate the chi-squared statistic, take the difference between a pair of observed (O) and expected values (E), square the difference, and divide that squared difference by the expected value. Repeat this process for all cells in your contingency table and sum those values. The resulting value is χ^2. We'll calculate it for our example data shortly!

Important Considerations about the Chi-Squared Statistic

Please note several important considerations about chi-squared values:

Zero represents the null hypothesis. If all your observed frequencies equal the expected frequencies exactly, the chi-squared value for each cell equals zero, and the overall chi-squared statistic equals zero. Zero indicates your sample data exactly match what you'd expect if the null hypothesis is correct.

Squaring the differences ensures both that cell values must be non-negative and that larger differences are weighted more than smaller differences. A cell can never subtract from the chi-squared value.

Larger values represent a greater difference between your sample data and the null hypothesis. Chi-squared tests are one-tailed tests rather than the more familiar two-tailed tests. The test determines whether the entire set of differences exceeds a significance threshold. If your

χ^2 passes the limit, your results are statistically significant! You can reject the null hypothesis and conclude that the variables are dependent—a relationship exists.

Calculating Chi-Squared for our Example Data

Let's calculate the chi-squared statistic for our example data! To do that, I'll rearrange the contingency table, making it easier to illustrate how to calculate the sum of the squared differences.

Uniform	Status	Observed	Expected	Squared difference/ Expected
Blue	Dead	7	12.65	2.52
Blue	Alive	129	123.35	0.26
Gold	Dead	9	5.12	2.94
Gold	Alive	46	49.88	0.30
Red	Dead	24	22.3	0.13
Red	Alive	215	216.77	0.01
			Sum	6.17

The first two columns indicate the combination of categorical variable values. The next two are the observed and expected values that we calculated before. The last column is the squared difference divided by the expected value for each row. The bottom line sums those values.

Our chi-squared test statistic is 6.17. Ok, great. What does that mean? Larger values indicate a more substantial divergence between our observed data and the null hypothesis. However, the number by itself is not useful because we don't know if it's unusually large. We need to place it into a broader context to determine whether it is an extreme value.

Using the Chi-Squared Distribution to Test Hypotheses

One chi-squared test produces a single chi-squared value. However, imagine performing the following process.

First, assume the null hypothesis is valid for the population. At the population level, there is no relationship between the two categorical variables. Now, we'll repeat our study many times by drawing many random samples from this population using the same design and sample size. Next, we perform the chi-squared test of independence on all the samples and plot the distribution of the chi-squared values. This distribution is known as a sampling distribution, which is a type of probability distribution.

If we follow this procedure, we create a graph that displays the distribution of chi-squared values for a population where the null hypothesis is true. We use sampling distributions to calculate probabilities for how unlikely our sample statistic is if the null hypothesis is correct.

Fortunately, we don't need to collect many random samples to create this graph! Statisticians understand the properties of chi-squared distributions so we can estimate the sampling distribution using the details of our design.

Our goal is to determine whether our sample chi-squared value is so rare that it justifies rejecting the null hypothesis for the entire population. The chi-squared distribution provides the context for making that determination. We'll calculate the probability of obtaining a chi-squared value that is at least as high as the value that our study found (6.17), which is the P-value! A low probability indicates that our sample data are unlikely when the null hypothesis is true.

Graphing the Chi-Squared Test Results for Our Example

For a table with r rows and c columns, the method for calculating degrees of freedom for a chi-square test is (r-1) (c-1). For our example, we have two rows and three columns: (2-1) * (3-1) = 2 df.

The following graph displays the chi-squared distribution for our study's design.

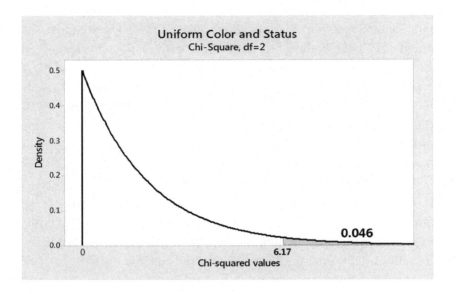

The distribution curve displays the likelihood of chi-squared values for a population where there is no relationship between uniform color and status. I shaded the region that corresponds to chi-square values greater than or equal to our study's value (6.17). When the null hypothesis is correct, chi-square values fall in this area approximately 4.6% of the time, which is the p-value (0.046). With a significance level of 0.05, our sample data are unusual enough to reject the null hypothesis.

The sample evidence suggests that a relationship between the variables exists in the population.

Bonus Analysis!

But wait! There's more to this story! The bonus lesson is that it is vital to include the genuinely pertinent variables in the analysis. Perhaps the color of the shirt is not the critical variable but rather the crewmember's work area. Crewmembers in Security, Engineering, and Operations all wear red shirts. Maybe only security guards have a higher death rate?

We can test this theory using the 2 Proportions test. We'll compare the fatality rates of red-shirts in security to red-shirts who are not in security.

The summary data are below. In the table, events are the number of deaths, while trials are the number of personnel.

	Events	Trials
Security	18	90
Not security	6	149

```
Test and CI for Two Proportions

Sample   X     N   Sample p
1       18    90   0.200000
2        6   149   0.040268


Difference = p (1) - p (2)
Estimate for difference:   0.159732
95% CI for difference:   (0.0712689, 0.248194)
Test for difference = 0 (vs not = 0):   Z = 3.54   P-Value = 0.000

Fisher's exact test: P-Value = 0.000
```

The p-value of 0.000 signifies that the difference between the two proportions is statistically significant. Security has a mortality rate of 20% while the other red-shirts are only at 4%.

Security officers have the highest mortality rate on the ship, closely followed by the gold-shirts. Red-shirts that are not in security have a fatality rate like the blue-shirts.

As it turns out, it's not the color of the shirt that affects fatality rates; it's the duty area. That makes more sense.

Risk by Work Area Summary

The Chi-square test of independence and the 2 Proportions test both indicate that the death rate varies by work area on the U.S.S. Enterprise. Doctors, scientists, engineers, and those in ship operations are the safest with about a 5% fatality rate. Crewmembers that are in command or security have death rates that exceed 15%!

Categorical Variables and Discrete Distributions

In chapter 10, you learned how continuous data have a distribution of values. Similarly, categorical variables have a distribution of values. However, it's a discrete probability distribution where each level of the categorical variable is associated with a probability.

For the Star Trek example, one categorical variable was uniform color, which has the distribution of values for the categories.

Uniform Color	Proportion
Gold	0.128
Blue	0.316
Red	0.556

To determine whether the distribution of categorical data follow the values that you expect, you can perform the Chi-Square Goodness-of-Fit Test. This test is very similar to the Poisson version in Chapter 12 except that you must specify the test proportions.

When you draw a random sample, you can determine whether the proportions in your sample fit a distribution of values you expect. For this test, we'll again turn to the Chi-square goodness-of-fit test to determine whether your data fit a particular discrete probability distribution. These tests compare the theoretical frequencies to the frequencies of the observed values. If the difference is statistically significant, you can conclude that your data do not follow that specific discrete distribution.

Chi-square goodness-of-fit tests have the following hypotheses.

- **Null**: The sample data follow the hypothesized distribution.
- **Alternative**: The sample data do not follow the hypothesized distribution.

For goodness-of-fit tests, small p-values indicate that you can reject the null hypothesis and conclude that your data were not drawn from a population with the specified distribution. Consequently, goodness-of-fit tests are a rare case where you look for high p-values to identify candidate distributions.

Analyze the CSV file that contains the data for both examples: DiscreteGOF.

I'll walk you through an example. It is easy to perform this test.

Car Color Example of a Discrete Distribution

PPG Industries studied the paint color of new cars bought in 2012 for the entire world. We want to assess whether the distribution of car colors in our local area follows the global distribution. In this example, the PPG data are real, but I'm making up our local data. Car color is our categorical variable and the levels are the individual colors.

After gathering a random sample of the color of cars sold in our state, we enter the observed data and global proportions in a worksheet like this:

Color	OurState	Global Proportions
White	120	0.22
Silver	114	0.20
Black	92	0.19
Gray	86	0.12
Red	34	0.09
Brown	33	0.08
Blue	47	0.07
Green	11	0.02
Other	2	0.01

The OurState column contains the tally for each color that we observed. The PPG Industries data are in the Global Proportions column.
We'll perform the Chi-square goodness-of-fit test to determine
whether our local distribution is different than the global distribution.
We'll use the PPG proportions as the test proportions.

The Chi-Square Goodness-of-Fit Test Results

Chi-Square Goodness-of-Fit Test for Observed Counts: OurState

```
Using category names in Color


                           Test                Contribution
Category   Observed   Proportion   Expected        to Chi-Sq
White           120         0.22     118.58          0.01700
Silver          114         0.20     107.80          0.35659
Black            92         0.19     102.41          1.05818
Gray             86         0.12      64.68          7.02756
Red              34         0.09      48.51          4.34014
Brown            33         0.08      43.12          2.37510
Blue             47         0.07      37.73          2.27757
Green            11         0.02      10.78          0.00449
Other             2         0.01       5.39          2.13212

   N   DF    Chi-Sq    P-Value
 539    8   19.5887      0.012
```

This goodness-of-fit test compares the observed proportions to the
test proportions to see if the differences are statistically significant.
The p-value is less than the significance level of 0.05. Therefore, we

can conclude that the discrete probability distribution of car colors in our state differs from the global proportions.

In the table, the Contribution to Chi-squared column tells us which paint colors contribute the most to the statistical significance. Gray and Red are the top two colors, but we don't know the nature of how they contribute to the difference.

Let's compare the observed and expected values chart to see how these values are different.

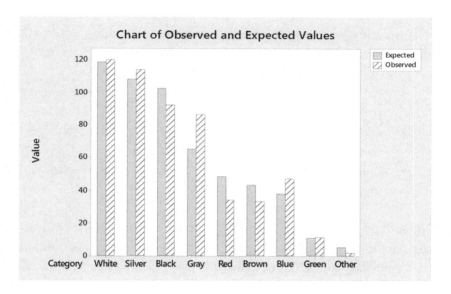

The chart indicates that the observed number of gray cars is higher than expected. On the other hand, the observed number of red cars is less than expected.

Overall, we can conclude that the difference between the proportions of local car colors and global car colors is statistically significant. Grey cars are overrepresented locally while red cars are underrepresented.

Review and Next Steps

Throughout this chapter, we covered different ways to analyze categorical data. You learned about the chi-square test of independence, which determines whether a relationship exists between two categorical variables. Then, we used the chi-square test again to determine whether the distribution of categorical values followed an expected distribution.

Because of the importance of the chi-square test for categorical data and Poisson data, I showed you how it works in detail.

The main differences between these forms of the chi-square test are the values that you use as the expected values.

- Poisson goodness-of-fit tests calculate expected values using the Poisson distribution.
- Tests of independence calculate expected values that represent no relationship between the variables.
- Chi-square goodness-of-fit tests use expected values that you supply.

Up until this point, we've been looking at parametric hypothesis testing. These tests make assumptions about the probability distribution that your data follow. Notice how for every test so far, I've always mentioned one probability distribution or another. However, another type of hypothesis test does not assume your data follow a particular distribution. Statisticians call this nonparametric hypothesis testing. In the next chapter, I provide an overview of nonparametric tests.

CHAPTER 14

Alternative Methods

Throughout this book, we've been looking at parametric hypothesis testing. This type of testing uses sampling distributions to calculate probabilities and determine statistical significance, such as the t, F, binomial, Poisson, and chi-square distributions. Obtaining valid results for these tests can depend on whether your data follow a specific distribution, such as the normal distribution. Although, we saw how you can waive that assumption in some cases.

There is another type of hypothesis test that does not assume your data follow a particular distribution. Statisticians call this nonparametric hypothesis testing. While these tests don't require your data to follow a specific distribution, there are other assumptions.

In this final chapter, I provide an overview of nonparametric testing and compare it to the more common parametric methods. We'll start with nonparametric tests that assess the medians. Then, we'll move onto bootstrapping, which is a nonparametric method that creates sampling distributions using a resampling method that is entirely different from those using probability distributions.

Nonparametric Tests vs. Parametric Tests

Nonparametric tests don't require your data to follow the normal distribution. They're also known as distribution-free tests and can provide benefits in certain situations. Typically, analysts are more comfortable with parametric tests than nonparametric tests.

If you've heard of these tests, you've probably heard it's best to use nonparametric tests if your data are not normally distributed—or something along these lines. That seems like an easy way to choose, but there's more to the decision than that.

In this section, I compare the advantages and disadvantages of using the following types of hypothesis tests:

- Parametric analyses to assess group means
- Nonparametric analyses to assess group medians

I'd like you to focus on one key reason to perform a nonparametric test that doesn't get the attention it deserves. I'll get to that later on!

Related Pairs of Parametric and Nonparametric Tests

Nonparametric tests are a parallel universe to parametric tests. In the table, I show corresponding pairs of tests.

Parametric tests of means	Nonparametric tests of medians
1-sample t-test	1-sample Sign, 1-sample Wilcoxon
2-sample t-test	Mann-Whitney test
One-Way ANOVA	Kruskal-Wallis, Mood's median test
Factorial DOE with a factor and a blocking variable	Friedman test

Advantages of Parametric Tests

Advantage 1: Parametric tests can provide trustworthy results with distributions that are skewed and nonnormal

Many people aren't aware of this fact, but parametric analyses can produce reliable results even when your continuous data are nonnormally distributed. You just have to be sure that your sample size meets the requirements for each analysis in the next table. Simulation studies have identified these requirements. You might recognize these values from the previous chapters that cover the assumptions for each test.

Parametric analyses	Sample size requirements for nonnormal data
1-sample t-test	Greater than 20
2-sample t-test	Each group should have more than 15 observations
One-Way ANOVA	• For 2-9 groups, each group should have more than 15 observations • For 10-12 groups, each group should have more than 20 observations

You can use these parametric tests with nonnormally distributed data thanks to the central limit theorem.

Advantage 2: Parametric tests can provide trustworthy results when the groups have different amounts of variability

It's true that nonparametric tests don't require normally distributed data. However, nonparametric tests have the disadvantage of an additional requirement that can be very hard to satisfy. The groups in a nonparametric analysis typically must all have the same variability (dispersion). Nonparametric analyses might not provide accurate results when variability differs between groups.

Conversely, parametric analyses, like the 2-sample t-test or one-way ANOVA, allow you to analyze groups with unequal variances. In most statistical software, it's as easy as checking the correct box! You don't have to worry about groups having different amounts of variability when using parametric analyses.

Advantage 3: Parametric tests have greater statistical power

In most cases, parametric tests have more power. If an effect actually exists, a parametric analysis is more likely to detect it.

Advantages of Nonparametric Tests

Advantage 1: Nonparametric tests assess the median which can be better for some study areas

Now we're coming to my preferred reason for when to use a nonparametric test. The one that practitioners don't discuss frequently enough!

For some datasets, nonparametric analyses provide an advantage because they assess the median rather than the mean. The mean is not always the better measure of central tendency for a sample. Even though you *can* perform a valid parametric analysis on skewed data, that doesn't necessarily equate to being the better method. Let me explain using the distribution of salaries.

Salaries tend to be a right-skewed distribution. The majority of wages cluster around the median, which is the point where half are above and half are below. However, there is a long tail that stretches into the higher salary ranges. This long tail pulls the mean far away from the central median value. The two distributions are typical for salary distributions.

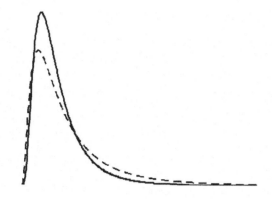

These two distributions have roughly equal medians but different means.

In these distributions, if several very high-income individuals join the sample, the mean increases by a significant amount even though incomes for most people don't change. They still cluster around the median.

In this situation, parametric and nonparametric test results can give you different results, and they both can be correct! For the two distributions, if you draw a large random sample from each population, the difference between the means is statistically significant. Despite this, the difference between the medians is not statistically significant. Here's how this works.

For skewed distributions, changes in the tail affect the mean substantially. Parametric tests can detect this mean change. Conversely, the median is relatively unaffected, and a nonparametric analysis can legitimately indicate that the median has not changed significantly.

You need to decide whether the mean or median is best for your study and which type of difference is more important to detect.

Advantage 2: Nonparametric tests are valid when your sample size is small and the data are potentially nonnormal

Use a nonparametric test when your sample isn't large enough to satisfy the size requirements in the previous table and you're not sure that your data follow the normal distribution. Be aware that normality tests can have insufficient power to produce useful results with small samples. In this situation, they can fail to detect substantial departures from the normal distribution.

This situation is difficult. Nonparametric analyses tend to have lower power at the outset, and a small sample size only exacerbates that problem.

Advantage 3: Nonparametric tests can analyze ordinal data, ranked data, and outliers

Parametric tests can analyze only continuous data and the findings can be overly affected by outliers. Conversely, nonparametric tests can also analyze ordinal and ranked data, and not be tripped up by outliers. Sometimes you can legitimately remove outliers from your dataset if they represent unusual conditions. However, sometimes outliers are a genuine part of the distribution for a study area, and you should not remove them.

You should verify the assumptions for nonparametric analyses because the various tests can analyze different types of data and have differing abilities to handle outliers.

If your data use the ordinal Likert scale and you want to compare two groups, read the next section about which analysis you should use to analyze Likert data.

Advantages and Disadvantages of Parametric and Nonparametric Tests

Many people believe that choosing between parametric and nonparametric tests depends on whether your data follow the normal distribution. If you have a small dataset, the distribution can be a deciding factor. However, in many cases, this issue is not critical because of the following:

- Parametric analyses can analyze nonnormal distributions for many datasets.
- Nonparametric analyses have other firm assumptions that can be harder to meet.

The answer is often contingent upon whether the mean or median is a better measure of central tendency for the distribution of your data.

- If the mean is a better measure and you have a sufficiently large sample size, a parametric test usually is the better, more powerful choice.
- If the median is a better measure, consider a nonparametric test regardless of your sample size.

Lastly, if your sample size is tiny, you might be forced to use a nonparametric test. It would make me ecstatic if you collect a larger sample for your next study! As the table shows, the sample size requirements aren't too large. If you have a small sample and need to use a less powerful nonparametric analysis, it doubly lowers the chance of detecting an effect.

Analyzing Likert Scale Data

Likert scales are the most broadly used method for scaling responses in survey studies. Survey questions that ask you to indicate your level of agreement, from strongly agree to strongly disagree, use the Likert scale.

The data in the worksheet are five-point Likert scale data for two groups.

Group 1	Group 2
1	3
3	5
4	5
2	4
5	3
3	2
3	4
2	5
4	3
3	4

Likert data seem ideal for survey items. However, there is considerable debate over how to analyze these data because they are ordinal. The general question centers on whether you should use a parametric or nonparametric test to analyze Likert data.

Most people are more familiar with using parametric tests. Unfortunately, Likert data are ordinal, discrete, and have a limited range. These properties violate the assumptions of most parametric tests. The highlights of the debate over using each type of analysis with Likert data are as follows:

- Parametric tests assume that the data are continuous and follow a normal distribution. Although, with a large enough sample, parametric tests are valid with nonnormal data. The 2-sample t-test is a parametric test.
- Nonparametric tests are accurate with ordinal data and do not assume a normal distribution. However, there is a concern that nonparametric tests have a lower probability of detecting an effect that exists. The Mann-Whitney test is an example of a nonparametric test.

What is the best way to analyze Likert scale data? This choice can be a tough one for survey researchers to make.

Studies have attempted to resolve this debate once and for all. Unfortunately, many of these studies assessed a small number of Likert distributions, limiting the generalizability of the results. Recently, more powerful computers have allowed simulation studies to analyze a broad spectrum of distributions.

In this section, I highlight a study by de Winter and Dodou. They conduct a simulation study that assesses the capabilities of the Mann-Whitney test and the 2-sample t-test to analyze five-point Likert scale data for two groups. Let's find out if one of these statistical tests is better to use! (DeWinter & Dodou, 2010)

The investigators assessed a group of 14 distributions of Likert data that cover the gamut. The computer simulation generated independent pairs of random samples that contained all possible combinations of the 14 distributions. The study produced 10,000 random samples for each of the 98 combinations of distributions. Whew! That's a lot of data!

The study statistically analyzed each pair of samples with both the 2-sample t-test and the Mann-Whitney test. Their goal is to calculate the error rates and statistical power of both analyses to determine whether one is better for Likert data. The project also looked at different sample sizes to see if that made a difference.

Comparing Error Rates and Power When Analyzing Likert Scale Data

After analyzing all pairs of distributions, the results indicate that both types of analyses produce type I error rates nearly equal to the target value. A type I error rate is essentially a false positive. The test results are statistically significant but, unbeknownst to the investigator, the null hypothesis is true. This error rate should equal the significance level.

The 2-sample t-test and Mann-Whitney test produce nearly equal false-positive rates for Likert scale data. Further, the error rates for both analyses are close to the significance level target. Excessive false positives are not a concern for either hypothesis test.

Regarding statistical power, the simulation study shows that there is a minute difference between these two tests. Apprehensions about the Mann-Whitney test being underpowered were unsubstantiated. In most cases, if there is an actual difference between populations, the two tests have an equal probability of detecting it.

There is one qualification. A power difference between the two tests exists for several specific combinations of distribution pairs. The difference in power affects only a small portion of the possible combinations of distributions. My suggestion is to perform both tests on your Likert data. If the test results disagree, look at the article to determine whether a difference in power might be the cause.

In most cases, it doesn't matter which of the two statistical analyses you use to analyze your Likert data. If you have two groups and you're analyzing five-point Likert data, both the 2-sample t-test and Mann-Whitney test have nearly equivalent type I error rates and power. These results are consistent across group sizes of 10, 30, and 200.

Sometimes it's just nice to know when you don't have to stress over something!

Example of the Mann-Whitney Median Test

Time for another Mythbusters experiment! To paraphrase the show, I don't just talk about the hypotheses; I put them to the test! The Mythbusters present the data they collect, and I've entered them in this CSV data file: BattleSexes.

We'll test the myth that women multitask better than men. To determine whether this is true, ten men and ten women perform a standard set of tasks that require multitasking. The Mythbusters create a scoring system that measures how well each subject performs the tasks. The scores can range from 0 to 100.

The average score for women is 72, and for men it is 64. The Mythbusters state that this eight point difference confirms that women are better at multitasking.

This study is an excellent example of when you should use a hypothesis test to draw conclusions from data—except they didn't use one. Let's see if the proper hypothesis test agrees with their conclusion!

Choosing the Correct Hypothesis Test

The multitasking study seems to call for a 2-sample t-test because we want to compare the means of two groups. However, I performed a normality test, which indicates that these data don't follow the normal distribution.

Nonnormal data aren't always a show-stopper for parametric tests like t-tests. However, because the sample size is less than 15 per group, nonnormal data are a problem for us. We can't trust the results from a 2-sample t-test.

Instead, we'll need to use a nonparametric test to compare the medians. The Mann-Whitney test allows us to compare the medians for two groups.

The Mann-Whitney Test Results

```
┌─────────────────────────────────────────────────────────────────┐
│  Mann-Whitney Test and CI: Female Multitask, Male Multitask       │
│                                                                   │
│                        N   Median                                 │
│  Female_Multitask  10    75.00                                    │
│  Male_Multitask    10    55.00                                    │
│                                                                   │
│                                                                   │
│  Point estimate for η1 - η2 is 10.00                              │
│  95.5% Percent CI for η1 - η2 is (-9.99, 30.01)                  │
│  W = 120.0                                                         │
│  Test of η1 = η2 vs η1 ≠ η2 is significant at 0.2730             │
│  The test is significant at 0.2542 (adjusted for ties)           │
└─────────────────────────────────────────────────────────────────┘
```

The p-value is 0.2542 and the confidence interval contains zero. Both conditions indicate that the test results are not significant. We have insufficient evidence to conclude that the women's median score is greater than the men's median. The confidence interval contains negative values, which tell us that we should not be surprised if a replicate study found that men had a higher median!

The Mythbusters saw the eight point difference between the sample means and "confirmed" the myth. Unfortunately, the hypothesis test reveals that the sample evidence is not strong enough to draw this conclusion. The effect is not large enough to be distinguishable from random sampling error.

Bootstrapping Method

Bootstrapping is a statistical procedure that resamples a single dataset to create many simulated samples. This process allows you to calculate standard errors, construct confidence intervals, and perform hypothesis testing for numerous types of sample statistics. Bootstrap methods are alternative approaches to parametric hypothesis testing and are notable for being easier to understand and valid for more conditions.

In this section, I explain bootstrapping basics, compare bootstrapping to parametric statistical methods, and explain when it can be the better method. Additionally, I'll work through an example using real data to create bootstrapped confidence intervals.

Both bootstrapping and parametric methods use samples to draw inferences about populations. To accomplish this goal, these procedures treat the single sample that a study obtains as only one of many random samples that the study could have collected.

From a single sample, you can calculate a variety of sample statistics, such as the mean, median, and standard deviation—but we'll focus on the mean here.

Suppose an analyst repeats their study many times. In this situation, the mean will vary from sample to sample and form a distribution of sample means. Statisticians refer to this type of distribution as a sampling distribution. As you've seen throughout this book, sampling distributions are crucial because they place the value of your sample statistic into the broader context of many other possible values.

While performing a study many times is infeasible, both parametric tests and bootstrapping methods can estimate sampling distributions. Using the larger context that sampling distributions provide, these procedures can construct confidence intervals and perform hypothesis testing.

Differences between Bootstrapping and Parametric Hypothesis Testing

A primary difference between bootstrapping and traditional statistics is how they estimate sampling distributions.

Parametric hypothesis testing procedures require equations for probability distributions that estimate sampling distributions using the sample data's properties, the experimental design, and a test statistic. To obtain valid results, you'll need to use the proper test statistic and satisfy the assumptions. That's the process I've described in detail throughout this book.

The bootstrap method uses an entirely different approach to estimate sampling distributions. This method takes the sample data that a study obtains and then resamples it over and over to create many simulated samples. Each of these simulated samples has its own properties, such as the mean. When you graph the distribution of these means on a histogram, you can observe the sampling distribution of the mean. You don't need to worry about test statistics, formulas, and assumptions.

The bootstrap procedure uses these sampling distributions as the foundation for confidence intervals and hypothesis testing. Let's look at how this resampling process works.

How Bootstrapping Resamples Your Data to Create Simulated Datasets

Bootstrapping resamples the original dataset with replacement many thousands of times to create simulated datasets. This process involves drawing random samples from the original dataset. Here's how it works:

1. The bootstrap method has an equal probability of randomly drawing each original data point for inclusion in the resampled datasets.
2. The procedure can select a data point more than once for a resampled dataset. This property is the "with replacement" aspect of the process.
3. The procedure creates resampled datasets that are the same size as the original dataset.

The process ends with your simulated datasets having many different combinations of the values that exist in the original dataset. Each simulated dataset has its own set of sample statistics, such as the mean, median, and standard deviation. Bootstrapping procedures use the distribution of the sample statistics across the simulated samples as the sampling distribution.

Example of Bootstrap Samples

Let's work through an easy case. Suppose a study collects five data points and creates four bootstrap samples, as shown below.

Original	Bootstrap1	Bootstrap2	Bootstrap3	Bootstrap4
1	1	2	1	1
2	1	3	2	1
3	3	3	3	1
4	3	3	5	4
5	5	4	5	5

This simple example illustrates the properties of bootstrap samples. The resampled datasets are the same size as the original dataset and only contain values that exist in the original set. Furthermore, these values can appear more or less frequently in the resampled datasets than in the original dataset. Finally, the resampling process is random and could have created a different set of simulated datasets.

Of course, in a real study, you'd hope to have a larger sample size, and you'd create thousands of resampled datasets. Given the enormous number of resampled data sets, you'll always use a computer to perform these analyses.

How Well Does Bootstrapping Work?

Resampling involves reusing your one dataset many times. It almost seems too good to be true! In fact, the term "bootstrapping" comes from the impossible phrase of pulling yourself up by your bootstraps! However, using the power of computers to randomly resample your one dataset to create thousands of simulated datasets produces meaningful results.

The bootstrap method has been around since 1979, and its usage has increased. Various studies over the intervening decades have determined that bootstrap sampling distributions approximate the correct sampling distributions.

To understand how it works, keep in mind that bootstrapping does not create new data. Instead, it treats the original sample as a proxy for the real population and then draws random samples from it. Consequently, the central assumption for bootstrapping is that the original sample accurately represents the actual population.

The resampling process creates many possible samples that a study could have drawn. The various combinations of values in the simulated samples collectively provide an estimate of the variability between random samples drawn from the same population. The range of these potential samples allows the procedure to construct confidence intervals and perform hypothesis testing. Importantly, as the sample size increases, bootstrapping converges on the correct sampling distribution under most conditions.

Now, let's see an example of this procedure in action!

Example of Using Bootstrapping to Create Confidence Intervals

For this example, I'll use bootstrapping to construct a confidence interval for a dataset that contains the body fat percentages of 92 adolescent girls. I used this dataset in the section about identifying the distribution of your continuous data. These data do not follow the normal distribution. Because it does not meet the normality assumption of traditional statistics, it's a good candidate for bootstrapping. Although, the large sample size lets us bypass this assumption. The histogram displays the distribution of the original sample data.

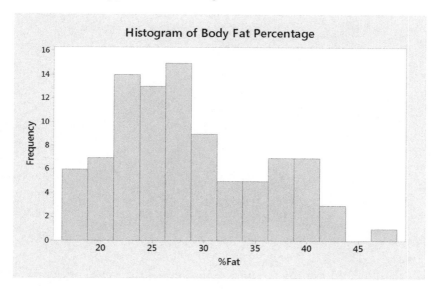

Use the CSV dataset to try it yourself: body_fat.

Performing the bootstrap procedure

To create the bootstrapped samples, I'll use Statistics101 again, as I did for illustrating the central limit theorem.

Using its programming language, I've written a script that takes my original dataset and resamples it with replacement 500,000 times. This process produces 500,000 bootstrapped samples with 92 observations in each. The program calculates each sample's mean and plots the distribution of these 500,000 means in the following histogram. Statisticians refer to this type of distribution as the sampling distribution of means. Bootstrapping methods create these distributions using resampling, while traditional methods use equations for probability distributions.

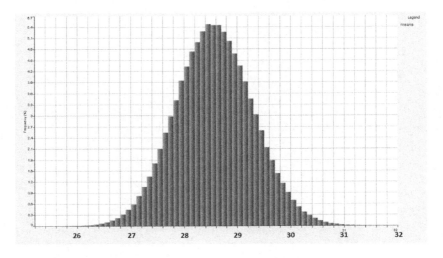

It's hard to determine from the screenshot, but the sampling distribution centers on 28.55. To create the bootstrapped confidence interval, we simply use percentiles. For a 95% confidence interval, we need to identify the middle 95% of the distribution. To do that, use the 97.5th percentile and the 2.5th percentile (97.5 – 2.5 = 95). In other words, if we order all sample means from low to high, and then chop off the lowest 2.5% and the highest 2.5% of the means, the middle 95% of the means remain. That range is our bootstrapped confidence interval!

For the body fat data, the program calculates a 95% bootstrapped confidence interval of the mean [27.16 30.01]. We can be 95% confident that the population mean falls within this range.

This interval has the same width as the traditional confidence interval for these data, and it is different by only several percentage points. The two methods are very close.

Notice how the sampling distribution in the histogram approximates a normal distribution even though the underlying data distribution is skewed. This approximation occurs thanks to the central limit theorem. As the sample size increases, the sampling distribution converges on a normal distribution regardless of the underlying data distribution (with a few exceptions).

Benefits of Bootstrapping over Traditional Statistics

Dear readers, I hope by now you know that I love intuitive explanations of complex statistical methods. And, bootstrapping fits right in with this philosophy. This process is much easier to comprehend than the equations required for probability distributions that parametric methods use. However, bootstrapping provides more benefits than just being easy to understand!

Bootstrapping does not make assumptions about the distribution of your data. You merely resample your data and use whatever sampling distribution emerges. Then, you work with that distribution, whatever it might be, as we did in the example.

Conversely, the traditional methods often assume that the data follow the normal distribution or some other distribution. For the normal distribution, the central limit theorem might let you bypass this assumption when you have a large enough sample size. Consequently, you can use bootstrapping for a wider variety of distributions, unknown distributions, and smaller sample sizes. Sample sizes as small as 10 can be usable.

In this vein, all traditional methods use equations that estimate the sampling distribution for a specific sample statistic when the data follow a particular distribution. Unfortunately, formulas for all combinations of sample statistics and data distributions do not exist! For example, there is no known sampling distribution of medians for some distributions, which makes bootstrapping the perfect analyses for it. Other analyses have assumptions such as equality of variances. However, none of these issues are problems for bootstrapping.

For Which Sample Statistics Can I Use Bootstrapping?

While this overview focuses on the sample mean, the bootstrap method can analyze a broad range of sample statistics and properties. These statistics include the mean, median, mode, standard deviation, analysis of variance, correlations, regression coefficients, proportions, odds ratios, variance in binary data, and multivariate statistics among others.

There are several, mostly esoteric, conditions when bootstrapping is not appropriate, such as when the population variance is infinite, or when the population values are discontinuous at the median. And, there are various conditions where tweaks to the bootstrapping process are necessary to adjust for bias. However, those cases go beyond the scope of this introduction.

Wrapping Up

Whew! We covered a lot in this book! This book serves as an introduction to hypothesis testing. Hypothesis tests are powerful tools that let you use relatively small samples to draw conclusions about entire populations.

My goal for this book was to provide you with the knowledge to understand how these tests work, know when to use each type of test, use them properly to obtain trustworthy results, and to interpret the results correctly. I also wanted you to know how to use a wide variety of tests that assess various characteristics of different types of data.

Review of What You Learned in this Book

We started by learning why you even need to use hypothesis testing. If you're working with a representative sample, you can use it to obtain estimates of population parameters but they will contain random sampling error. The population estimates from your sample are unlikely to equal the actual population parameters. That's true whether you are estimating means, variability, correlations, proportions, counts, and so on. It's also true if you're estimating those properties for a single population or comparing them between populations. You can't take your sample estimates at face value.

All hypothesis tests assess the following two hypotheses:

- **Null**: The effect or relationship does not exist in the population.
- **Alternative**: The effect/relationship does exist in the population.

Hypothesis testing provides tools that take your sample data, incorporate sampling error, and draw inferences about populations.

Significance levels: The evidentiary standard for how strong your evidence must be.

P-values: Measures the strength of your evidence against the null hypothesis.

Statistical Significance: If your p-value is less than your significance level, your results are statistically significant. You can reject the null hypothesis and conclude that the effect or relationship you see in your sample also exists in the population.

Confidence Intervals: A range of values that is likely to contain the population parameter. If your results are statistically significant, the confidence interval will exclude the null hypothesis value, which is often zero for no effect.

After learning about the need to use hypothesis tests and the tools they provide, we moved on to several examples of t-tests that compare one or two group means. You also got your first look at the assumptions for hypothesis tests that we must satisfy to obtain reliable results.

Then, we dug into the mechanics of how they work: tests statistics, sampling distributions, and calculating probabilities to determine statistical significance. We studied these concepts in-depth for means and t-tests, but they apply to other sample characteristics and other probability distributions that we covered later on.

We paid particular attention to interpreting p-values correctly because analysts misinterpret them so frequently. P-values measure the strength of the evidence against the null hypothesis. The lower the p-value, the less compatible your data are with the null hypothesis.

Remember, p-value calculations assume the null is true. They don't assess the probability that either the null or alternative hypothesis are correct. Instead, p-values represent the probability of obtaining the sample effect your study observed, or more extreme, if the null hypothesis is true.

Up next, I covered the two types of errors in hypothesis testing:

- **Type I**: Rejecting a true null hypothesis (i.e., false positive).
- **Type II**: Fail to reject a false null hypothesis (i.e., false negative).

You can manage Type I errors simply by setting the significance level. The significance level, also known as alpha, equals the Type I error rate. However, managing Type II errors is a bit more involved. You reduce false negatives by increasing the statistical power of your test.

Statistical power is the probability of detecting an effect that actually exists. Typically, the most practical way to increase power is by increasing sample size. Gauging a suitable sample size involves estimating the effect size and data variability, and specifying the statistical power you want. Then your software will calculate the necessary sample size.

We moved on to looking at other facets, such as one- and two-tailed hypothesis tests. Remember, avoid using one-tailed tests as a way to increase power! We looked at the concept of degrees of freedom and how that ties into different probability distributions. You also saw how simulations show that sampling distributions will approximate the normal distribution when you have a sufficiently large sample size—just as the central limit theorem states! This property allows us to waive the normality assumption for some hypothesis tests when the sample size is large enough.

Next, we covered a whole bunch of hypothesis tests and incorporated everything we learned up to this point. I broke them down by type of data and characteristic you want to test. Additionally, I showed you how these tests use the F, binomial, Poisson, and chi-square distributions to calculate probabilities and determine statistical significance.

- Continuous data
    - ANOVA: At least three means—both one-way and two-way.
    - Post Hoc tests: Use after ANOVA to assess specific pairs of groups.
    - Variances tests: Assess variability in one or two groups.
    - Correlation: Determine whether a linear relationship exists between two continuous variables.
    - Distribution: Assess the type of distribution that your data follow.
- Binary data
    - Proportions tests: Assess the proportion of events in one or two groups.
- Count data
    - Poisson rate tests: Assess the rate of occurrence in one or two groups.

- o   Poisson Goodness of Fit Test: Determine whether your count data follow the Poisson distribution.
- Categorical data
  - o   Test of Independence: Determine whether a relationship exists between two categorical variables.
  - o   Chi-square Goodness of Fit Test: Determine whether the proportions of categorical values fit a distribution that you specify.

Finally, we took a brief look at alternate methodologies. The bulk of this book covers parametric tests. These tests assume your sample data come from populations adequately modeled by probability distributions with a set of parameters. However, there are nonparametric tests that assess the median. These tests don't assume your data follow a specific distribution but do have other assumptions. Bootstrapping methods use a resampling with replacement technique that estimates sampling distributions without using probability distributions.

Hypothesis Tests by Data Types

Continuous Data

What you're testing	Hypothesis Test
One mean to reference value	1-sample t-test (p36)
Means for two groups	2-sample t-test (p40), Paired t (p45), Comparing CIs (p53)
Means for at least three groups	One-Way ANOVA (p193), Two-Way ANOVA (p220)
Compare specific groups from ANOVA	Post hoc tests (p205), Tukey's Method (p211), Dunnett's Method (p216), Hsu's MCB (p217)
One standard deviation to reference value	1 Sample Variance Test (p233)
Standard deviations for two groups	2 Sample Variance Test (p236)
Correlation between two continuous variables	Pearson's correlation coefficient (p239)
Shape of distribution	Distribution tests for continuous data (p242)
Presence of outliers	Outlier test (p268)
Medians	Nonparametric tests (p332), Mann-Whitney Test (p340)

Binary Data

What you're testing	Hypothesis Test
One proportion to a reference.	1 Proportions Test (p275)
Proportions for two groups.	2 Proportions Test (p278)

Count Data

What you're testing	Hypothesis Test
One rate to a reference.	1 Sample Poisson Rate Test (p301)
Rates for two groups.	2 Sample Poisson Rate Test (p303)
Do your counts follow the Poisson distribution?	Poisson Goodness-of-Fit Test (p306)

Categorical Data

What you're testing	Hypothesis Test
Association between two categorical variables.	Chi-Squared Test of Independence (p311)
Do the proportions of values follow a hypothe-sized distribution?	Chi-Square Goodness-of-Fit test (p326)

Ordinal and Ranked Data

What you're testing	Hypothesis Test
Medians, Ordinal and Ranked data	Nonparametric tests (p332), Mann-Whitney Test (p340)
Various	Bootstrapping Methods (p342)

My Other Books

Introduction to Statistics: An Intuitive Guide

Learn statistics without fear! Build a solid foundation in data analysis. Be confident that you understand what your data are telling you and that you can explain the results to others! I'll help you intuitively understand statistics by using simple language and deemphasizing formulas.

This guide starts with an overview of statistics and why it is so important. We proceed to essential statistical skills and knowledge about different types of data, relationships, and distributions. Then we move to using inferential statistics to expand human knowledge, how it fits into the scientific method, and how to design and critique experiments—whether it's your own or another researcher's.

Learn the fundamentals of statistics in this 255 page book:

- Why is the field of statistics vital in our data-driven society?
- Interpret graphs and summary statistics.
- Find relationships between different types of variables.
- Understand the properties of data distributions.
- Use measures of central tendency and variability.
- Interpret correlations and percentiles.
- Use probability distributions to calculate probabilities.
- Learn about the normal and binomial distributions in depth.
- Grasp the differences between descriptive and inferential statistics.
- Use data collection methodologies properly and understand sample size considerations.
- Access free downloadable datasets so you can try it yourself.

Currently available as an ebook and in print!
Learn more on my website: statisticsbyjim.com/store

Jim Frost

Regression Analysis: An Intuitive Guide

Over the course of this full-length book, you'll progress from a beginner to a skilled practitioner. I'll help you intuitively understand regression analysis by focusing on concepts and graphs rather than equations and formulas. I use everyday language so you can grasp regression at a deeper level.

Learn practical tips for performing your analysis and interpreting the results. Feel confident that you're analyzing your data properly and able to trust your results. Know that you can detect and correct problems that arise.

This 336-page book covers the following:

- How regression works and when to use it.
- Selecting the correct type of regression analysis.
- Specifying the best model.
- Understanding main effects, interaction effects, and modeling curvature.
- Interpreting the results.
- Assessing the fit of the model.
- Generating predictions and evaluating their precision.
- Checking the assumptions and resolving issues.
- Downloadable datasets for the examples.
- Examples of different types of regression analyses.
- Access free downloadable datasets so you can try it yourself.

Currently available as an ebook and in print!
Learn more on my website: statisticsbyjim.com/store

References

You can find formulas and references for the information in this book in most statistics textbooks. I use the *Statistics* by Freedman et al. listed below. The other references apply to journal articles that I use to make specific points throughout this book.

Beran, J., Vesikari, T., Wertzova, V., Karvonen, A., Honegr, K., Lindblad, N., . . . Devaster, J. (2009). Efficacy of inactivated split-virus influenza vaccine against culture-confirmed influenza in healthy adults: a prospective, randomized, placebo controlled trial. *J Infect Dis*, 1861-9.

Cumming, J., & Finch, S. (2005). Inference by Eye: Confidence Intervals and How to Read Pictures of Data. *American Psychologist*, 170-180.

DeWinter, J., & Dodou, D. (2010). Five-Point Likert Items: t test versus Mann-Whitney-Wilcoxon. *Practical Assessment, Research and Evaluation*, 1-16.

Freedman, D., Pisani, R., & Purves, R. (1998). *Statistics* (3rd ed.). New York: W.W. Norton & Company.

Goldstein, H., & Healy, M. J. (1995). The Graphical Presentation of Means. *Journal of the Royal Statistical Society*, 170-180.

Monto, A., Ohmit, S., Petrie, J., Johnson, E., Truscon, R., Teich, E., . . . Victor, J. (2009). Comparative efficacy of inactivated and live-attenuated influenza vaccines. *N Engl J Med*, 1260-7.

Open Science Collaboration. (2015). Estimating the reproducibility of pyschological science. *Science*.

Shiffler, R. E. (1988). Maximum Z Scores and Outliers. *The American Statistician*, 79-80.

Recommended Citation for This Book

Frost, J. (2020). Hypothesis Testing: An intuitive guide for making data driven decisions. Statistics By Jim Publishing.

Index

About the Author

I'm Jim Frost, and I have extensive experience in academic research and consulting projects. In addition to my statistics website, I am a regular columnist for the American Society of Quality's *Statistics Digest*. Additionally, my most recent journal publication as a coauthor is *The Neutral Gas Properties of Extremely Isolated Early-Type Galaxies III* (2019) for the American Astronomical Society.

I've been the "data/stat guy" for research projects that range from osteoporosis prevention to analysis of online user behavior. My role has been to design the proper research settings, collect a large amount of valid measurements, and figure out what it all means. Typically, I'm the first person on the project to learn about new findings while interpreting the results of the statistical analysis. Even if the findings are not newsworthy, that thrill of discovery is an awesome job perk!

I love statistics and analyzing data! I've been performing statistical analysis on-the-job for 20 years and helping people learn statistics for over ten years at a statistical software company. I love talking and writing about statistics.

I want to help you learn statistics. But I'm not talking about learning all the equations. Don't get me wrong. Equations are necessary. Equations are the framework that makes the magic, but the truly fascinating aspects are what it all means. I want you to learn the true essence of statistics. I'll help you intuitively understand statistics by focusing on concepts and graphs. Although, there might be a few equations!

I've spent over a decade working at a major statistical software company. When you work on research projects, you generally use a regular group of statistical analyses. However, when you work at a statistical software company, you need to know of all the analyses that are in the software! I helped people use our software to gain insights and maximize the value of their own data regardless of their field.

While working at the statistical software company, I learned how to present statistics in a manner that makes statistics more intuitive. I'll be writing about my experiences and useful information about statistics. However, I'll focus on teaching the concepts in an intuitive way and deemphasize the formulas. After all, you use statistical software so you don't have to worry about the formulas and instead focus on understanding the results.

Statistics is the field of learning from data. That's amazing. It gets to the very essence of discovery. Statistics facilitates the creation of new knowledge. Bit by bit, we push back the frontier of what is known. That is what I want to teach you! My goal is to help you to see statistics through my eyes—as a key that can unlock discoveries that are in your data.

The best thing about being a statistician is that you get to play in everyone's backyard. —John Tukey

I enthusiastically agree! If you have an inquisitive mind, statistical knowledge, and data, the potential is boundless. You can play in a broad range of intriguing backyards!

That interface between a muddled reality and obtaining orderly, valid data is an exciting place. This place ties together the lofty goals of scientists to the nitty-gritty nature of the real world. It's an interaction that I've written about extensively in this book and on my blog, and I plan to continue to do so. It's where the rubber meets the road.

One of the coolest things about the statistical analysis is that it provides you with a toolkit for exploring the unknown. Christopher Columbus needed many tools to navigate to the New World and make his discoveries. Statistics are the equivalent tools for the scientific explorer because they help you navigate the sea of data that you collect.

The world is becoming a progressively data-driven place, and to draw trustworthy conclusions, you must analyze your data properly. It's surprisingly easy to make a costly mistake. Even if you're not performing your own studies, you'll undoubtedly see statistical analyses conducted by others. Can you trust their results or do they have their own agenda?

Just like there were many wrong ways for Columbus to use his tools, things can go awry with statistical analyses. I'm going to teach you how to use the tools correctly, to draw the proper conclusions, and to recognize the conclusions that should make you wary!

You'll be increasingly thankful for these tools when you see a worksheet filled with numbers and you're responsible for telling everyone what it all means.

Read more on my website: statisticsbyjim.com

Printed in Great Britain
by Amazon

11274104R00220